CLEAN

the (mis)adventures of
an alcoholic drug addict

MICHAEL REBELLINO

LUMINARE PRESS
WWW.LUMINAREPRESS.COM

A WORK OF FICTION
INSPIRED BY TRUE EVENTS

Names, characters, places, and incidents have been altered and
molded by the author's imagination and are neither represented
nor intended to be a literal account of people or events.
Though the story may read like a memoir,
the details are fiction and not fact.

Luminare Press
442 Charnelton St.
Eugene, OR 97401
www.luminarepress.com

LCCN: 2021909374
ISBN: 978-1-64388-607-7

for RMA

CONTENTS

FOREWORD

(in four words)

people are just people

ANOTHER FOREWORD

(in another four words)

why are you afraid?

STAGE ONE

(denial)

in the beginning

it was fun
carefree
innocent
safe

actually—

not safe
not at all

felt safe to me

my friends and i
wild and free
expanding our minds
learning to be

we were young

the invincible ones

in the middle

it was (mostly) fun
(sometimes) carefree
(not as) innocent

still safe

actually—

still not safe
not at all

felt safe enough

my friends and i
we knew what was what
had it all figured out
not a doubt in our minds

we were still so young

wide-eyed and alive

in the end

it was Valentine's Day

but i'm getting ahead of myself

the story starts in a room

i've been a thousand times
a thousand lines to come alive
i've lived a thousand lives

i die a little every time

here i am again
in this room, this heaven
to come alive

to die

in this room, this hell

a glass table
smudged and dusty
musty smoke smell
masked with incense
cigarette ash scattered
tattered wood floors
once white door, white walls
now dirty
peeling ceiling
window blinds closed tight
only light—the TV, muted
shoes still on
sprawled out on the couch
a faded, walnut-brown
ceiling fan's blades oscillate
round and round
the only sound

in this room, i wait

the dopeman's always late

i always wait

in this room

this purgatory

the story really starts in a car

over ten years prior

one night with some friends
someone said, *i got that fire*

i'd seen the egg in the frying pan

"just say no" supposedly the plan

c'mon, Uncle Sam, you can keep your scare tactics

let's see what happens
if i just say yes

i like fried eggs

pass me the light, i said

hit the bowl like *this ain't my first time*

then choked like *i'm lyin'*

truth is, i hated it that night
didn't even get high

so i tried it again

the second time was when
i got high for the first time

weed is all i need, i thought

but, g r a d u a l l y

then all-of-a-sudden

it wasn't enough

the story prob'ly starts even earlier

on some dumb Freudian or Jung psychoanalytic tip
pick from the list of umpteen witty derivatives
something pretty, like "cognitive dissonance"

i'm a mental patient, here come the aliens
paranoid schizophrenic, certified insane
lock me up, pump me full of drugs

speaking of, how can the problem be the solution too?
and i'm the one who's crazy?
gimme a break

all i can say is i'm here now
who cares how i got this way?

it's bigger than me anyway
someone else's fault most likely
maybe it all happened despite me

whatever, what's done is done
i was bored one night, so i got high

no rhyme or reason
no comprehensive explanation
no psychiatric evaluation required

i'm tired of all the questions

for all intents and purposes, let's just agree—

the story starts in a room
a car
the womb

or somewhere in-between

by the way

my name's Cameron

i'll be your guide for the duration of this adventure
but i'd prefer that you consider me a friend

God knows i need more of them

i don't have a map or template
no formal training or expertise
no letters after my name
no related degrees

what i *do* have is a stack of paper
a sixty-pack of cheap pens
a heap of legal stimulants
and nowhere to be

not to mention this relentless, festering *itch*

so sit back, relax, and enjoy the ride
it may get bumpy up ahead
i apologize in advance

i hope we can still be friends

you may elect to remain seated
with your seat belt securely fastened
but do as you wish

smoking is ~~prohibited~~ encouraged

the first time i got high

we buy an eighth
from a guy named Jake

seeds, stems, and shake
migrate from the bag
to the blunt, stuffed tight

who's got the light?

puff, puff, pass
pitch-black backroads at night
bumpin' Outkast, windows cracked

no navigation on our phones
destination unknown
just drive

until the weed's gone
and we see neon
the sign beaming light
into the night sky

tacos! someone yells

you already know, the driver replies

i walk inside, slowly
find a seat without ordering

two of the guys, laughing at the counter
pronouncing names of menu items, laughing louder

they finally order and sit down

how was it? i ask

great, my one friend says with a cheese-faced grin

i don't even remember what i ordered, the other says

i take a deep breath
float up to the register
completely forget how to speak

hello, sir, the cashier says

she knows we're high, i think

what would you like? she asks

same thing, i say

blank stare from the cashier

as him, i add, pointing back to the table

just then my other friend—the driver—comes in
head down, eyes fixated on his hands, cupped at his chest

literally overflowing with change

he looks up at me, eyes so red i think they're bleeding
we both immediately explode with laughter

i make a beeline back to my seat
hear the change clink clink clink

i turn around, see him laying it down
a small mountain on the counter

how many tacos can i get with this? he asks

the cashier, not even surprised
a look of *not this again* in her eyes

Cheese Face and I-Don't-Even-Remember-What-I-Ordered
back at the table, now a demolition zone

i sit down and douse whatever i got with hot sauce
barely taking the wrapper off
my taste buds can't get enough

the Change Monster saunters up
drops twelve tacos onto the table
sits down without saying a word

he proceeds to eat each taco in two bites, lightning speed
the rest of us watching, amazed, like *is he for real?*
he's unphased, like *what's the big deal?*

a dozen tacos disappear in two minutes flat
he takes his first audible breath in as many seconds
more of a gasp

he sits back, looks up at us, one by one

you guys have any change? he asks

now we're all gasping

or at least a drink?

i offer him mine, still laughing

he coughs then takes a sip

i'm fine, thanks for asking, he says
passing the cup back to me, coughing again

sweet kid, i say
standing up to leave

we walk outside, back to the car
satisfied smiles, light on our feet

a sparkling trail of loose change
like tiny islands, leading the way

leave it, someone says
breaking the silence

for next time

next time

my friends and i
drivin' around
gettin' high

our new routine

and then we creep into the parking lot
the driver—Cheese Face—turns the car off
flips his hood up over his head

let's beatbox before we go in, he says

dude in the passenger seat jumps right in
then Cheese Face, then me, then the rest of the back seat

no discussion needed, no dissenting opinion
all of us on a mission, single vision, lit

it prob'ly sounded like shit

after a minute or an hour, i don't really know
someone starts poundin' on the rear window

the rest of us stop

it's the guy in the back-left seat

what? he asks, still poundin' on the glass

percussion, he adds, *obviously*

aaaaand we're done, Middle Seat says

now we're standin' inside
five deep, sixteen years old

starin' at the menu board
kids in the candy store

such a momentous decision

we place our orders, one by one
one of everything under the sun

more composed than the last time

i feel much more in control

or at least more at peace
being out of control

which is sorta the same thing

    speaking of the last time, rabbit trail—

    it was never quite like that time again

    that first time feeling
    but a memory

    will i find it again, maybe even tonight?

    my friend
    my enemy

    or will it be a cold day in hell?

    end rabbit trail

we sit down with our food, everyone except Middle Seat
for some reason her order's taking longer
finally, around the corner, here she comes

i stop eating and watch her
beaming smile, childlike joy
her hair almost blowin' in the wind
yet it feels like slow motion

this should be a commercial for this place, i think

suddenly, her smile disappears
the tray, which she's holding with two hands
starts shaking, violently, totally unprovoked

nooooo! i see her eyes screaming, pleading

next thing i see—
cheeseburger, nuggets, fries
free falling, the tray capsized
drink cup exploding on impact with the floor
blast radius every square inch of the store

she's still holding the now empty tray
walking boldly through the carnage
like nothing happened

she sits down next to me, stares at her lap
i gently pry the tray from her petrified grasp

no one says a word

she looks up, slowly, face beet red

what should i do? she asks

we're all in tears

the fast-food crew snickers and sneers
roping off the area like a crime scene

Butterfingers apologizes, tries to help clean

no, please, one worker politely declines

i'm gonna wait in the car, she tells us

you want some of my fries? Window Beat asks

no, thank you, she says, *just the keys*

the rest of us finish our food then flee the scene

sorry, dudes! Cheese Face yells on the way out

hold up, i say, spinning around and heading back in

can i have some ice cream, please? i ask the cashier

i apologize again then leave

what the hell happened in there? i ask Butterfingers
laughing as i get into the car

is that mine?! she squeals with delight

i hand her the ice cream

careful, i say

her smile beams, her joy childlike

Window Beat starts banging on the glass

Cheese Face drives away, into the night

who's got the light? he asks

the first, next, and every time

flip a switch
a flick of the wrist
euphoric bliss

this, that, and the other

comfortable in my own skin
like never before

more

more

more

long story short—i was in love

that's where the story begins

STAGE TWO

(guilt)

love lost

waiting on a word

a word from her, my love

a whisper would be enough

hoping for a whisper

a whisper from her, my love

a sigh, a breath, a windblown touch

fading away in the silence

silence complete, yet empty

only darkness now

lonely darkness unending

praying for a sign, a sign from above

can you still hear me, my long-lost love?

crying out for something, something, anything at all

nothing

all there ever was

or will be to come

i hear a rustling

a far-off rustling in the dark

show yourself! i howl

whoever you are

i see a light

a glimmer of light, now a silhouette

my love, is it you?!

an air of hope in my breath

i feel a kiss

a kiss of wind on my cheek

if it's you, my love

i beg of you—speak

craving a word

a word from you, my love

craving, insatiable craving

for you and you alone, love

my soul is waiting

a letter i never sent

Dear Rachel,

I hope you're doing well and enjoying Portland. It's hard to believe it's been four months since you moved. Time sure flies, in hindsight at least.

Did you get my last letter? It's okay if you don't respond, but I hope you read it. I guess it doesn't really matter. I just wanted to say sorry. I never meant to hurt you. I guess that doesn't really matter either.

I'm not sure why I'm even writing this. You've made it quite clear you don't want to talk to me anymore. I just wanted you to know I'm sorry. I hate how things ended. It was probably for the best, though, like pulling off a Band-Aid—quick and painless. Well, it was quick.

I do genuinely hope you like Portland, and that it's feeling more and more like home as time goes on. Have you been to Powell's yet? It's this really cool bookstore that's like one of the biggest in the world or whatever, but you probably already knew that. Something about the smell of books and coffee always reminds me of home.

This letter sounds bitter and sad. I'm actually doing quite well overall, if I do say so myself. I have close to six months sober now. That's the truth.

Without you, I don't know if I would have made it to six weeks. Honestly. Maybe not even six days. So in case I never said it—thank you, Rachel. Truly, thank you.

I hope you have a Merry Christmas, and that you get to see your family. Or at least get to spend time with people that feel like family. Goodbye, Rachel.

Sincerely,
Cameron

thinking back to our first date

SCENE ONE

i tried to jump but stumbled out of my car
as you pulled up in yours

you parked and stepped out, gracefully, onto the gravel
laughing so contagiously, so full of life

looking into your eyes, i felt so light

you held my gaze with yours
i rose from all fours to standing

hi, i said with a smile

are you alright? you asked, still laughing

i smiled wider and nodded yes

you were even prettier in person
i tried my best not to stare

we hugged for the first time

you smelled like bubble gum and summer air

(i dared to think it was my last first date)

SCENE TWO

we walked to the trail you'd picked out to hike

i talked and you listened, laughed
asked such great questions

when it felt like i had talked forever
you talked and i listened

wanted to tell you, show you everything
to hear, see, feel everything you were telling me

wanted to know you, for you to know me

if someone were to read a transcript of our conversation
they'd think we were crazy

it made perfect sense to us

transitioning back and forth so casually
between the heart-to-heart and bizarre, so naturally

like our pasts and personalities were designed
for this very moment, when our paths combined

even the silence, though rare
was comfortable, shared

(the silence feels much different now)

SCENE THREE

we found some shade and sat down to take a break

you started picking paint chips from your hair
said you'd been painting your uncle's deck

i started helping, you stopped and watched
could feel your eyes on me, thoughtfully

sitting on that fallen tree, by the river, next to me
caked in sweat and paint, you looked so beautiful
unintentionally, you couldn't even help but be

long after i'd removed all the paint i could see
i kept fingering through your hair

lost in thoughts of what might be

i watched you smiling, staring off into the distance
wanted to kiss you right then and there

but i didn't

instead, i kept playing with your hair

amazed that something so simple
could be so intimate

(life's full of surprises, isn't it?)

SCENE FOUR

we rented kayaks to row down the river

spent twenty minutes trying to pay

there was no one in line, but we couldn't say one full sentence
without cracking up, riffing off each other

the front desk lady laughing with us

finally, we resorted to pointing and animal noises
then lollygagged our way into the river

i splashed you playfully
you laughed and splashed me back, almost tipping
then ran right into me, your kayak T-boning mine

our kayaks spinning out of control, frozen time

until we crashed into the brush jutting out of the bank

we laughed too hard to tell if we were hurt
turned out we weren't, both completely fine

kept rowing, slowly, down the river of diamonds

the water shining below and in front, all around us
guiding us, now coasting

floating like it was only us

(i haven't been kayaking since)

SCENE FIVE

i set up my hammock between two trees

we tried to lay inside, side by side, but it was too small

so you lay down, i sat on the ground nearby
gently rocking you back and forth

you singing some nursery rhyme, quietly
me listening, smiling

until the string snapped, the hammock collapsed
crashed to the ground, you trapped inside

the whole time, the only sound—your laughter
followed closely by mine, once i knew you were alright

you climbed out and said, *nice job tying the knot, dude*

we both laughed again

(you should see how good i can tie the knots now)

SCENE SIX

we had a picnic with the snacks you brought
cheese, crackers, grapes, whatnot

i told you more about my past

you just listened, intently, seeming to understand
as much as someone can who's never been through it

you said you were sorry, how hard it must be
how heartbreaking and lonely

i'm just happy you're doing better lately, you said

and now you have me

for better or worse?

in sickness and health?

'til death do us part?

(if only)

SCENE SEVEN

we started walking through the woods
back to our cars, it was nearly dark

i reached for your hand, slid my fingers between yours
you held mine tight, hand in hand we walked

not another soul in sight

out of nowhere, what sounded like a *neigh* broke the silence

a moment later, around the next corner, there came a horse
rider in tow, strutting slowly toward us

we must be on the horse trail…

oopsy-daisy, you said

the horse didn't seem to care, just trotted by and neighed

the rider, a look of disdain, was silent as they passed
we smiled back, then neighed at the same time, unplanned

the rider turned his head back, looking at us quizzically
and was nearly clotheslined by a low-hanging branch of a tree

i remember thinking, *i've laughed more today than in the past decade*

i'd never felt so alive, so awake

and i was stone-cold sober

(i hope i never forget that feeling)

SCENE EIGHT

i brought a couple things for you, you said
standing outside your car in the dark

i'd told you how often i drank chai tea
the first gift—chai-flavored lip balm

you were always listening, paying attention
i put some on, it tasted like heaven

the second gift—a blueberry doughnut with icing
you'd described it, at length, over the phone

i ate the whole thing right then and there
it was even more delicious than you'd said

i offered to share, you declined a bite
then licked the icing off my finger

i licked my lips, then almost tripped
as i leaned in, beneath the stars
and kissed you

then lingered, fractions of an inch from your lips

waiting

tasting blueberry and chai
tasting life itself, flavor-ized

pulled you closer, held you tight
breathed you in, tried to absorb you
the stars, everything, beneath my skin

kissed you again, longer this time

gently pulling your lips from mine
you whispered in my ear with such conviction

remember—there is hope...

no matter what...

there is always *hope*

i choked back the tears
tilted my head back, looked at the stars

then into your eyes, shining so brightly
your whole face glowing, like an angel, radiant

the image painted in my mind

i'll never forget it

(i can still hear you whispering)

SCENE NINE

we kissed again and i said, *goodbye*

for now, you said

when we both got home, we FaceTimed
it must have been close to midnight

me sitting on my bed, you laying in yours
i read to you over the phone

a children's story, *Blueberries for Sal*

i read 'til you fell asleep

you looked so peaceful

kept reading 'til i finished the book
then blew you a kiss goodnight

sweetest of dreams, my love, i whispered before i hung up

you, still asleep, stayed on the line

i smiled myself to sleep that night

(can't help but smile thinking about it now)

SCENE TEN (THE NEXT DAY)

that's never happened to me before
i've never fallen asleep on the phone...

your voice, it makes me feel...

safe, i guess, you do in general...

that was the best date i've ever had, you said

same, i said, *what a perfect day*

we agreed no one could top it
but we'd try on our next date

i can hardly wait, you said

i can't imagine a bad day
as long as we're together, i said

i almost said i love you

but decided to wait

(now it's too late)

slow me down

slowly drown the noise

'til only your voice abounds

surround me with your love

it's all around me now

our second date was even better

it's only fitting, Rachel said
since you like Blueberries for Sal *so much*
and the blueberry doughnut—this is where they make them!
i got here early and snagged one for you before they sold out!

thanks! i said, smiling as she handed me the doughnut

did you get one for yourself? i asked

shore did, but i already ate it

understandable, i said then took a bite

here, have some of mine

she hesitated then said, *okay!* and took a small bite

i could live off these things, i said, taking another bite

ummm—yes! she said

plus, a blueberry-picking adventure cannot begin
until you consume at least one fresh blueberry doughnut...

this is random, but my mom has a painting
of a young girl and boy, arms around each other
each of them holding a basketful of apples...

and the title is Apple Pals

that's cute, i said

you know what we are? she asked

what?

blueberry pals

fast forward

looks like you two have had a fun morning, the waitress said
smiling as she handed us each a menu

we shore have, Rachel said
smiling back at the waitress, then at me

blue stains caked on our faces and clothes
for the whole restaurant to see

can i start you off with a glass of wine?
perhaps a cosmo for the lady?

just water for me, please, Rachel said
not even glancing at the drink list

same, please, i said

you can get wine or something if you want, i said after the waitress left

it's okay, Rachel said

you can drink in front of me
i don't mind, really...

but i do appreciate the gesture
for real, it means a lot

Rachel smiled and said, *i know*

between the look on her face and her tone
those words carried weight like an oversize load

you had me at hello, i said

anywho, like i was saying earlier
my last relationship lasted a few years...

i thought he was the one...

we actually were engaged briefly...

but then i found out
he'd been cheating on me...

and, obviously, lying about it too...

so i left, Rachel said
looking down at the table

i'm sorry, i said
and i appreciate you telling me...

also, for the record, i don't look at you any differently
because you were engaged...

even if you'd gotten married, divorced, had kids
i'd still be sitting right here

well, in that case...

juuust kidding, she said, smiling

honestly, though, she continued, *it was for the best...*

and now you know why i live with my parents

i smiled

those big brown puppy eyes, she said
so sweet, so innocent...

those are the most dangerous kind

what shall we do? i asked, back at her parents' house
my eyes as big and sweet and innocent as could be

wanna make beds on the floor and watch Friends?

ummm—yes! i said, mimicking her reply from earlier

she laughed

you can go to sleep if you want, i said after the first episode

she'd been yawning

no, i'm not tired...

are you?

nope, not even a little bit

i put my arm around her
her head on my chest
our eyes on the screen

her head rising and falling, almost imperceptibly
with each breath, her hair smelled like vanilla bean

*as you know, my name's Rachel
but i'm totally Monica in this show*

*i just wanna stay awake
and lie here with you all night...*

Monica slash Rachel, i said

meeeee too, she said, yawning again

when i woke up, she was gone

sunlight pouring in through the blinds
noises coming from another room

hmmmmm, i sighed, rolling over

are you awake?! Rachel asked from somewhere

me sleepy, i said

i have a surprise! she yelled

coming, i mumbled

good morning, sunshine, i said as i walked into the kitchen
a few minutes later

hey, you, she said, turning around and smiling
then immediately turning back to the griddle

i hope you like pancakes!
and that's your coffee on the table

sure do, and thanks

good, because i may have made way too many, she said
you can take some home with you!

mmm, leftover pancakes, my favorite, i said
how'd you sleep?

wonderfully, you?

same, just not long enough

i actually feel pretty good, though, considering

i do too, i said, closing my eyes

i opened them to find a mile-high plate of pancakes
two inches from my face, swaying, leaning

surprise! Rachel screamed

is this gonna be enough? i asked

i told you! and this isn't even counting the rejects
i, of course, ate along the way

you do too much, Rachel, i said, smiling

i try, she said, smiling back

so, do you still wanna go to church with me? she asked

i'd love to

i need to start getting ready then
do you mind?

you're not gonna eat?

there were quite a few rejects

gotcha, yeah, do your thing
i'll be here having a pancake party

Rachel went into the first-floor bathroom
i kept eating 'til i heard her singing

amazing grace, how sweet the sound
that saved a wretch like me…

i once was lost, but now am found
was blind, but now i see [1]

i finished eating, did the dishes, got ready quickly
humming the song, *only slightly off-key*
as Rachel pointed out when she was done

then we left
she drove
i slept

wake up, sleepyhead, Rachel said, *we're here*

i was just praying, i said

church was church

afterward, we had lunch with Rachel's family
then we—Rachel and i—stood in her driveway
hugging, kissing, laughing in the sunshine

laughing from a place deep within
a place that'd been desert-dry
for quite some time
dormant, decaying
now coming alive

next thing i knew—

Rachel left

no hug

no kiss

not even a goodbye

her silence says enough

and rejection sucks

but

i got like six months sober now

somehow

someway

and life is good most days

i'm getting ahead of myself again

STAGE THREE

(bargaining)

back in the middle

when it was (mostly) fun

(sometimes) carefree

(not as) innocent

my friends and i

we were still so young

wide-eyed and alive

was it all a dream?

never-ending circles

wake up wanting
something, anything, everything
to chase away the nothingness

contemplate how to stop it

i know! grab a pill and pop it

remnants of yesterday on the nightstand
lick my finger, swipe the wood for a taste
the blue powder chalky on my tongue

stand up with haste
gotta get some more
more's never enough

what it do, cuz?

can i come through?

now i'm makin' moves
no time to waste

at the dopeman's now
can Roxy come out and play?

shooooot

better now
for now at least

high
low
repeat

blues make the blues go away
figure out another way another day

no money never stopped me before
i know how to beg, borrow, steal

ain't no thang

today i have what i need
don't need a damn thing

always get what i need
something, anything, everything

someday you won't

pshhh, whaddayou know?

sniff another for good luck

then another for i don't even know

ahhhhh

better now
for now at least

high
low
repeat

can't sleep or stay awake
can't eat or stay away

don't feel anything then feel everything
good thing these pills kill pain
i love the way they set me free

you say freedom, i say bondage
have you counted the cost?

painkillers create more pain in their wake...

and as long as we're being honest—
they don't merely kill pain

even if the pain isn't real, it's real to me
so bring on the chains

and as for death, it'd be a relief

you don't know me or what i need
to stay alive, you don't know my life
just because i'm middle class and white
doesn't mean my life's been easy
i've been through some shit, believe me—
parents divorced when i was five
molested by a babysitter at six
OCD tendencies by seven
molested again, ages eight, nine, and ten
started carrying a knife at eleven
never molested again

believe me yet?

smoked my first cigarette in seventh grade
smoked a pack a day by age thirteen

then came the booze and drugs
and i couldn't get enough
so fuck off, please
and lemme do me

it doesn't have to be this way

it's too late

this is the life i chose
there's no other way
so i do what i know

pop pop, sniff sniff

to remember, to forget

off to the loony bin
who's comin' with?

hmmmmm

better now
for now at least

high
low
repeat

knock, knock

who dis?

the devil, bitch

can't tell what's real from what's in my head
can't tell if i'm alive or dead
this surely isn't living
it's only getting worse
after a while, pain loses its hurt
eventually numbness hurts even worse

it all feels like too much
can't get out of this funk
don't know what to do
such a mystery
developing quite a history of misery
fantasize 'bout wizardry, superhero capabilities
overcome by responsibilities
humdrum search for tranquility
in all the wrong places
can't count on anyone
not even familiar faces

can't go on like this, can't stop
gimme another pill to pop, sniff, smoke, or shoot
need a pick me up, need to reboot

shooooot

better now
for now at least

high
low
repeat

pills to wake up
calm down
lift me up
knock me down

pills when the noise gets too loud
when i can't hear a sound

other pills when the pills i want aren't around

lately all you do is knock me down
don't want you around anymore
i'm leavin' you, i mean it this time

sick and tired of your tireless lies
my tired eyes playin' tricks on me
you aren't shit to me
we're done
history

then tell me why
there's another line
a cut-up straw in your hand?

make up your mind
you can't have it both ways
i am the i am [2]
amazing grace...

how dare you say you don't need me?
so beneath me, my slave, beseech me
i see that lingering look in your eyes...

you know you need me
you'll never leave me
put the straw to your nose
and inhale deeply

ahhhhh

better now

for now at least

high

low

repeat

silent night

all is calm

all is bright [3]

all upon a winter's night

lying on the couch
Dev sprawled out on the floor
watching a movie we've seen before

Dev falls asleep midway through
wide awake, i let it play

the copious amount of opiates
flowing through my veins
beginning to fade

my last 30 waits with the change in my jeans
the word "save" has escaped my vocabulary

take a dirty dollar bill from my wallet, place the pill in the middle
fold the bill hotdog-style, then the edges in toward the center

that's how you make a boat, cuz, i hear the dopeman say

i grab the hardcover book from the coffee table
place it on my lap, set the boat down on top of that
pick up the TV remote in my right hand
my left pressing the folded bill flat, the book in place
i crush the pill with a burst of quiet but forceful blows
toss the remote aside, unfold the edges of the bill
pick it up with my left hand, carefully, still folded hotdog-style
fetch a hollowed-out pen from my pocket with my right hand
use the pen to form an opening, the boat now the shape of a *V*
now i know my ABCs, next time won't you sing with me? [4]

one end of the pen positioned at the start of the line
i lean in, the other end of the pen rests inside my right nostril
i sniff with all my might, moving the pen down the line
from right to left, then back again

i tilt my head back and exhale through my mouth
none of the powder falls out of my nose
another big sniff with left nostril pinched
to get the rest of it down my throat

all is calm and bright again
the sweet and subtle drip

the whole operation takes fifteen seconds
a quarter of a minute to get to heaven

i look at Dev, still sound asleep

i'm sorry, i say under my breath

a whisper of nostalgia creeping in
seeping through the floor

we're kids again
not only brothers
but friends too

like we were back then

i have a sense of something, for a second
that resembles hope

i hope this movie never ends

the credits roll

figures

i lie back down on the couch

fading in and out

suspended in a daze
that space between

the only place i feel like me

i weigh a million pounds
and no more than an ounce

enchanted, time dances
an indeterminate amount
i've lain here on this couch

i have the answers i seek
past, present, eternity
i see, i know, i am
complete

within

without

still fading in and out

all is calm

all is bright

all upon a winter's night

breathing slowly

slowly

slowly

now only if i think about it

now only if i *really* think about it

i can't breathe! i shout
but it comes out a whisper

where's the clicker?! i lip-synch

frantic, panic-struck

fumbling for the remote

finally find it, pick it up
throw it—*hard*—at Dev

he makes an unintelligible sound

i can't breathe! i shout again
barely louder than the first time

whaddayou mean? Dev mumbles

i mean i can't breathe, i whisper as loud as i can

what should we do? he asks, jumping to his feet

Narcan, i gasp

what's that? he asks, turning on a light

hospital, i say, trying to stand up

can you walk? Dev asks

trying, i gasp

where are my keys?! someone screams

dizzy, stumbling toward the door

keep moving forward

who's talking?

almost there now

i'm scared

how...?

        fading

                fading

           fading

                      out

come to in a hospital bed

this'll be expensive
first thought through my head

not *where am i?*
what day is it?
am i okay?

prob'ly get another piece of paper
with **DRUG OVERDOSE** in big bold letters

another of those
add it to the collection

don't forget about the lecture

yeah, i know

it doesn't matter

i don't matter

shoulda let me die

better that way

oh, my dearest Cameron
you can't possibly wish that were true

how do you know?

so much for hope

don't be so conceited

did you even see it?

can you even see me?

believe me, you matter
you matter to me

yeah, right

i see you always, Cameron
even tonight—

in fact, especially *tonight*

you're wasting your time

nothing to see here

why are you chasing a lie?

everything's a lie

no

yes

no

shut up!

i need some rest

close your eyes, child

let me sleep

sleep, child, in heavenly peace

this time i will be

in control
in control
in control

...

next time

...

next time
i will be

...

in control
in control
in control

next time i will be   am   god

is there food in hell?

several overdoses later

ladle in a couple of arrests

sprinkle in the shame and regret

a pinch of hopelessness

a dash of delusion

mix it all together

spread it over a base of loneliness

top it all off with *this only gets worse*

stick it in the oven, let it churn

take it out barehanded

third-degree burns

eat it standing up

at the peak of a cliff

peek over the edge

i will give you all of this...

*all the kingdoms of the world
the power and the glory...*

if you, therefore, will worship me [5]

bon appétit

cigarette thoughts

back and forth

and back again

was that a bird?

suspended in time

no past, no future

no plans, no dreams

how many 30s left?

not enough

only plots and schemes

striving and conniving

need to find some money

no rest, no relief

this smoke is nice

these aren't cheap

each day, the chase

no beginning, no end

feels good outside, don't wanna go in

take a deep breath

enjoy the high

my stomach hurts

every day the same

wasn't s'posed to

be this way

can't even get high anymore

tolerance somethin' fierce

what's the point?

need a break

but then i'll get sick

good point

somethin' needs to change

i'm workin' on it

why's it such a fight?

it's my problem

i can quit, easy

don't need any of this shit

and if i don't quit

what's it to you?

it's my life

everyone tellin' me how to live it

mind your own damn business

leave me alone

i almost died

damn mosquitos

i'm a fighter

never felt

so alive

the nightlife

i'll be fine
i've always been
i'm fine now

it's okay
i'm okay
everything'll work out

no point in worrying
just stop thinking
try to get some sleep

tomorrow's a new day
it's not too late

what if it is?

it's not

what if i'm not fine at all?

i am

everything always works out

i'll be fine

nothing's fine

i'm okay

no, i'm not

not at all

is it morning yet?

a letter i found on my bed

Dear Cam,

You are my best friend, and even more than that, you are my brother. I have lived practically my entire life with you around, and I am so thankful to be able to say that. A lot of people never experience the blessing of having siblings, let alone siblings who are so close with one another and can experience life by each other's sides. I thank God every day for you, and I cannot even begin to imagine not having you in my life. Even the mere thought brings tears to my eyes and hints of the deepest sorrow and darkness, which I cannot even begin to describe and wish to never, ever experience. I love you with my whole heart and would die for you.

We've had a great life together so far, but even with the not-so-good times (Mom and Dad divorcing and things of that nature), nothing ever seemed really bad because I always had you right there next to me. You are the best older brother to me, and after seeing some of my friends and others who are older brothers to their siblings, none compare to you.

Since I can remember, I have looked up to you. Whether it's trying to be like you, wanting your approval, seeking your advice and guidance, bragging to my friends about you, or copying your newest interest, it's all because you are a really cool human being. You are one of the smartest people I know and not just academically speaking—anything you focus your mind on you are able to simply understand. You are so creative in all that you do; you can draw better than most people and your writing is the same. You have a one-of-a-kind personality, and I love just spending time talking with you about, honestly, anything. I know it's difficult for us, but once you overcome your feeling of shyness in a situation you capture the room. I love it when you are around during family gatherings because you Cameron-ize them. You make them so much more fun, interesting, and entertaining, and I couldn't imagine them without you.

I know you don't think you are, but you are so disciplined and strong-minded. You are loving, compassionate, caring, and generous; you are always willing to help others in need. You do little things here and there to help others even though most of the time they may go unnoticed. You have given me money when I needed it, not expecting a dime back.

You are the bravest person I know. I mean, you went to Ohio State (a school with sixty-thousand-plus students) even though none of your friends were going there, you moved to Chicago for more than a year without knowing anyone, and most importantly, you willingly took on the role of being an older brother to me and didn't just distance yourself. You were there for me at all the right times, whenever I needed you. Few older brothers can say the same. I could go on and on until my fingers fell off from pure exhaustion, but the point I am trying to make is that you are a beautiful person and are truly one of a kind. You automatically make life better just by being yourself.

But all of this goes away when you (and I) get high so often and surround our lives with pills and bad habits, afraid of being sober. Our current situation of getting pills so often is a scary one and a slippery slope that leads to nothing but sadness, loneliness, and darkness. You are slowly drowning out and suffocating the so many good qualities that you have, and I hate it.

I hate how irritable you are when you don't have them. I hate how down and emotionless you are when they're not around. I hate to see you throw all your money away on them, living paycheck to paycheck. I hate that those are all you think about on a daily basis. I hate how much you rely on them. I hate how controlled you are by them. I hate that you don't realize how much you mean to all of us. I hate what they do to your closest relationships. I hate that you feel you need them to escape yourself. I hate that you don't believe in yourself. I hate that you don't see yourself as the person above because you are that person, but pills are slowly taking that away.

I know you have been living like this for a lot longer than I have, so I cannot fully comprehend the challenges you face on a day-to-day basis, but I know that you have the qualities to overcome this, and I can help with what I do know. You have all the resources you need around you to move toward a better direction. You don't have to do it alone as the older brother. That's what younger brothers are for, to pick the older up when he needs help. It's my turn to step up, and after all, you have shown me how to do that so well many times before.

I know it seems like an impossible task to overcome (ten-plus years of addiction), but what does that really mean when compared to the years that lay ahead? And what is impossible to God? The past means nothing; it is only the days ahead that hold meaning. You can accomplish, with God's help, anything you put your heart and mind toward. God has amazing and even seemingly impossible plans for you, Cam, and I have no doubt in my mind that you will figure out what those are, and you will succeed. You will be able to overcome the grip that pills have had on you for so many years. Let's surrender our lives to God and see where He takes us.

It will undoubtedly be difficult at times, but saying no to those temptations just once makes it easier and easier for all the next. We can learn how to live sober and learn to find joy in life without side help; we have each other and we have God. And once we do, we will never have experienced happiness like what will come. I don't want to waste another day of my life. We have endless, exciting opportunities and experiences to explore in our lives, and I would love for you, the you above, to be there right by my side.

I will do my best to help you (and myself) overcome this pickle we find ourselves in. But when times are tough and you are being tempted to give up, just remember all the great qualities that you have. You will overcome this. I love you more than words can express, and I would like nothing more in life than for you to go back to being the person that you once were, the person that you still are deep down. Remember, Cam, you are strong enough, brave enough, and disciplined enough to break free from this addiction. And when you feel like you are not, I will be there, and God will be there.

Love,
Your Best Friend, Your Brother,
Dev

sometimes

you need a third-person point of view

it's hard to see the problem

when the problem

convinces you it's the solution too

Dev

my best friend, my brother
three years younger

had just graduated from UC
aerospace engineering degree

when he moved in with me

one day, i asked him point-blank

wanna come with me to see an old friend?
aka, the dopeman

he resisted, i persisted
wouldn't give in, until he did

tricks of the trade, one might say

i hate that i…

i mean, he'd done drugs before

just not in a while

never the harder stuff

some role model, huh?

but i needed money and he had it

my name is Cameron

am i an addict?

other times

you need a few third-person points of view

it was October when i found the letter

Dev got sober

i didn't

whatever

in January, there was an intervention

next thing i remember—

we were on our way

it all happened so fast

how quickly life can change

STAGE FOUR

(depression)

the nightlife (rehab edition)

open the Bible my mom made me bring
the one my grandma gave me
when i was a baby

instinctively flip to Psalm 23 [6]
Mom used to read it to me
when i'd had a bad dream

sweat drips onto the page and bleeds

the Lord is my shepherd
i lack nothing
he makes me...

of course, my roommate snores
where's this Valium?

lie down in green pastures
he leads me beside...

here it is—10 milligrams

only one? i ask the nurse with my eyes

she nods subtly, knowingly

okay, i say out loud

she watches 'til it's down
makes me open my mouth to show her
then turns to leave

thanks, i say before she steps into the hall

she looks over her shoulder, into my eyes

get some sleep, sweetie, she says, smiling faintly

then she's gone

he leads me beside quiet waters
he refreshes my soul...

this snoring, though

he guides me along the right paths
for his name's sake...

i'll be up all night

even though i walk through the darkest valley
i will fear no evil...

it smells like piss in here

set the Bible down, open, on the bed
grab my coat, step into the hall, turn left
head toward the courtyard
i passed it on the way in

now i'm chain-smoking with the insomniacs
so much for this pack lasting a few days

i'm about to head back
someone new steps out
we make eye contact

he's clean-cut, forty-something
asks for a light
strikes up a conversation

ev'rybody calls me Angelo

yo, i'm Cameron, i say

i'm in for booze, he says
how's about you?

same, i guess
pills too

you new? he asks

yeah, just got here tonight

i'da guessed it, you got that deer-in-the-headlights thing goin' on

i wasn't s'posed to come 'til Monday

what gives?

they called me about a bed openin' up
said i had to come tonight or they'd give it to someone else

you alright, kid? you're bobbin' and weavin'

fine, just kinda drunk
and a lotta pills...

kinda freaked out when i got that call, ya know?

shit, man, sorry, i say
i shouldn't be talkin' 'bout that stuff

all good, kid

i light up another smoke
don't say much else
he doesn't need my help
to keep the convo going

couple weeks ago, Angelo starts another story
talking with his hands, animated, Italian accent

beautiful Sunday afternoon
i'm outside, doin' some work at the house...

he takes a long drag off his cigarette

cleanin' out the gutters
i'm up there on my ladder
my son's outside watchin' me
the dog's around somewhere
i'm pullin' out leaves, sticks, buncha junk
i shit you not—a newspaper
paper boy's got a helluva arm, huh?!
i turn around to check on my son...

he looks behind him as he says this

he's kneelin' down, diggin' in the mulch
the dog—Blackjack's his name—trots over
starts gettin' set up behind my son
i'm thinkin' not again
my dog's a humper...

Angelo hits his cigarette, slowly, letting that sink in

sure 'nuff, Blackjack mounts my son...

Angelo's kneeling down, acting this out

starts goin' to town...

he's vigorously dry humping the air

Blackjack, no! *i'm yellin' from the ladder*
dog pauses, looks up, starin' me in the eye...

then keeps right on goin'
yeah, buddy, i'm mad now
Blackjack, get off him!

i'm hollerin' and climbin' down the ladder...

once i'm on the ground, Blackjack hauls ass
my son lookin' at me, scared to death
that son of a bitch, Blackjack
humpin' ev'rything...

Angelo takes a deep drag

done the same with my leg...

another deep drag

pillows—shit, man, anything...

he finishes his cigarette
flicks it onto the concrete

it's somethin' else...

alright, man, i'm hittin' the sack

'night, i say

see ya 'round, kid

i wait 'til he's out of view
then walk to my room

i lie back down in bed
pick up the open Bible

i will fear no evil
for you are with me
your rod and your staff
they comfort me...

sounds like it's raining
maybe i'll go back out

you prepare a table before me
in the presence of my enemies
you anoint my head with oil...

Valium doin' its thing

my cup overflows...

fighting urge to sleep

surely your goodness and love will follow me
all the days of my life...

don't wanna wake up tomorrow
sober, in this place

and i will dwell in the house of the Lord forever

close Bible
put it on nightstand
turn light off
pull sandpaper sheet up to chin
close eyes
roll onto side
plastic pillow crunch, crunch, crunching
get as comfy as i'm gonna get
Valium helps

drifting off

Blackjack, no!

i laugh out loud, snapping me back

maybe this won't be so bad

yeah, right, it'll be worse than i think

i've tried everything else

i need to be here

lucky to be

i gotta get outta here

how?

    too tired to think now

        drifting off again

            tomorrow i'll…

                drifting

           figure this…

        drifting

          out

what withdrawal feels like

Everett

i remember when we met

it was lunchtime, my fifth day in
i glimpsed a new guy, about my age
him and his tray, heading my way

what's up, dude? i'm Everett

nishe-ta-meet-ya, i mumbled through a mouthful of pizza
then started choking

cool if i sit here? he asked, laughing

ahem, i cleared my throat, nodding my head yes

i'm Cameron, this your first day?

is it that obvious?

this place isn't that big

facts, how long you been in?

got here Sunday night

first time?

yup, you?

second, the first didn't stick, obviously...

whatchu in for? he asked

mainly pain pills, and drinking, you?

it'd be easier to tell you what i'm not *in for
i'm like a human garbage dumpster, bro*

i remember we met back up, later that night

felt like ninety-nine guys in a line in the hall
war stories flying like flags, a real junkie pride parade
all glorifying the past like they wanted to go back

i wanted to ask, *how'd that work out for you, dawg?*
look around—you forget where you are?

wanna go do somethin' else? i whispered to Everett instead

dude, i'm tryin' to hear what happened to Tony
after he drove his car into the living room, he said

my bad, i said, laughing

yes, please, get me outta here, stat, he said

my room's down the hall, we could play a game?

sounds good, i'd rather do literally anything than listen to this
i think that same dude was here last time

we left the parade and found the game shelf

ever played? i asked, pointing to Scrabble

sure have, and i'm 'bouts to kick yo' ass

you're on, my friend

i grabbed the tattered box, we walked to my room
closed the door, set up the board on the twin bed
a black plastic chair on each side

your move, i said

played two games, each won one
started a third, hardly laid a word

spinnin' stories of our own
we both just lost interest

even forgot, for a minute, where i was

was it unfair to judge those other guys so quickly?

are we really that different?

addiction's a bitch, an indiscriminate affliction
no matter how you spin it

forgive me, my fellow prisoners

i remember that Sunday, family visitation day
neither of our families came

no lectures or group, nothing we had to do
from noon 'til dinner, we were free

it was winter in Northeast Ohio
but you'd never have known

we spent the entire time outside
smoking, talking, tossing the football, walking around the pond

whatchu gonna do when you get outta here? Everett asked

i guess, go back to work...

and, ya know, try to stay sober, i said with a nervous laugh

that's awesome your job's gonna let you come back...

you doin' aftercare or anything? he asked

no, prob'ly not...

gonna be livin' with my brother, i said

he sober?

he drinks, but he's not one of us

that's a good start...

this shit's a lot different without these walls...

trust me

how long were you sober after your first time here?

few weeks

what happened? i asked

i don't know, man, nothin' really...

one day i woke up and decided to have a drink
yada yada, a few months passed...

and here i am, Everett said

does it feel...

i don't know, different now? i asked

yeah, for sure, i want it this time...

goin' back out was...

shit, man, i don't even know where to start
i'll just say it wasn't good

what're you gonna do after this? i asked

got a three-quarter house lined up back home
be there for a while, find a job, meetings...

i'd like to get back into music stuff...

beyond that, i don't really know, man
thought about movin' to Canada
workin' at my parents' farm up there...

i need a change of scenery, he said

is the grass greener in Canada?

ha ha, very funny

i'm just playin', man

i know, he said

but seriously, though, that sounds lovely...

can i come?

Everett laughed

speaking of your parents, what do they think about all this? i asked

they're just thrilled, he said

i laughed

no, but they've been super supportive
doin' whatever they can to help me
they mean well, and i'm grateful for 'em...

they just don't understand, man...

what about your parents? Everett asked

pretty much the same, i said

it can be frustrating, but how could they understand? he asked
how could anyone who hasn't been through it?

i mean, shit, man, we *don't even understand it...*

how can we expect the normies to get it?

normies? i asked

yeah, ya know, people that aren't like us, he said

i see, i said, chuckling at the term

for real, though, i don't wanna keep usin' this disease as an excuse
i don't wanna keep hurtin' every single person in my life...

i don't wanna lose anyone else...

your parents gonna come at all? he asked

they're comin' next week, my brother too, i said

that's what's up...

shit sucks, but it's for the best...

*then again, my parents came every Sunday last time
and here we are, round two...*

so who the hell knows?

i don't ever wanna come back here, i said
no offense

you're good, man, no one does...

*most people don't wanna come the first time either
but what else can we do?*

*learn to drink and do drugs responsibly
like the normies,* i suggested

*good luck with that, son
shit's impossible for people like us...*

you ever done it? Everett asked

even once?

i remember

        sitting by the pond

     watching the ripples glisten

   sun setting in the distance

     the barren trees swaying

gently in the breeze

    the outside world—

           so far away

      beyond the trees

somebody told me

girls in rehab

wear long sleeves

even in the summer

a cravings letter to myself

If you're reading this letter, then you're likely having a craving or have had one recently. DO NOT ACT ON THIS CRAVING! It will pass. You do not have to act on every thought you have; if you act on this one, IT WILL KILL YOU. Now that you are clean, you have the power to choose. If you use, it is your choice to do so, which would be the worst choice you could possibly make right now. You will immediately lose the power of choice you've worked so hard for. Your addiction will take over, again. Remember how well that worked out last time?

It'll be different this time; I'll be able to maintain control, you're probably thinking at this point. That's your addiction talking, and those are lies. Do you really forget that easily? Remember all the guilt and shame? Remember how much you hated yourself? Remember how exhausting each and every waking moment was? Do you really want to go down that road again? It'll only be worse this time around.

And if you don't want to do it for you, then do it for your family. *But they won't find out this time.* Don't kid yourself; you're not as slick as you may think. You're lucky they've stuck by you through all the bullshit, all the pain and heartache, all the tears and worry. If you have any morsel of love, any ounce of respect for them, then you will not pick up again.

Are you willing to sacrifice everything for that one thing? Seriously? Even though that one thing hates you and is trying to kill you? Because drugs and alcohol WILL KILL YOU eventually, probably sooner than later, if you decide to use again.

Yeah, alcohol too. Don't even think about having a beer to take the edge off. I don't care if everyone else seems to drink; you are not everyone else. You are an addict and alcoholic, and you always will be. Don't you forget that, ever. One beer will turn into two, which will turn into those pills you really want and who knows what else.

I hope you're still reading; in fact, you better still be reading. Your life depends on it. Do I have your attention now? Good. Tell someone about this craving, RIGHT NOW! And if no one's around, pick up the damn phone that's probably sitting in your left pants pocket as we speak. Call someone—your sponsor, someone from the meetings you've been going to (you're still going, aren't you?), your family, a friend, anyone in your support group will suffice—and tell on yourself. Cravings are a normal part of recovery, so don't be afraid to talk about it.

I don't feel like talking to anyone. Aw, poor you. Then read a book, write, or get your ass to the gym that's only a stone's throw away. Take a walk. Clean the apartment. Go to a meeting. Do something, anything, except sitting there feeling sorry for yourself, letting your addict brain run with this craving. We both know how that's gonna turn out.

You've been clean for a while now, and I know you can stay clean for one more day. Don't think about tomorrow; focus on the here and now. Right here, right now, you can stay clean. That's all you have to do—stay clean, *just for today.*

Think about how much better your life's gotten since you've been clean. And it will continue to get better, if and only if you stay clean. But if you use...

Well, shit, if you use after everything you've read thus far, I don't even know what else to say.

the last thing i learned in rehab

your insurance only covers twenty-one days

graduation day

i'm gonna miss you, man, i said
hugging Everett goodbye
my parents waiting outside

ditto, sweet cheeks, Everett said
pinching my cheek and winking

seriously, though, let's stay in touch, i said
and try to meet up once you're out

for sure, brother...

i'm gettin' a new number
but i'll hit you up, he said

sounds good

you should get a new number too

i will, my parents already brought it up...

welp, i guess it's about that time, i said

i'm really glad i met you, Everett

you too, homie, you too
you got this, my mutha fuckin' dude!

i can see it in your eyes, he said
you want this, and you have a reason, a why...

any time you're tempted, have a craving, whatever
just keep comin' back to the why...

and as they say, keep comin' back

guess i better get used to hearin' that, i said

you got this, my dude

i'll see you soon, i said, turning to leave

i paused at the door

the outside world much closer now
just beyond the glass

i looked over my shoulder, back at Everett

you got this, he said again

i took a deep breath
pushed the double doors open
stepped over the threshold

started walking toward my dad's car
him outside the driver's side
arms crossed, pacing back and forth

he smiled when he saw me

my mom in the passenger seat, she smiled too

i looked down at the concrete
kept walking, slowly

with each step, whispering, under my breath
i got this, i got this, i got this

like Everett said

twenty-three whispers
twenty-three steps
my trek complete

i inched the rear door open
my feet cement
frozen

i swiveled my head
looked back toward the building
hopin' to see Everett again

but didn't, not even a silhouette

i'm as ready as i'm gonna get...

i got this, i whispered again

another deep breath

pried my feet off the ground

and crept inside

the car door closed
like a coffin lid

the whole way home
a slow descent

into the earth

six feet of dirt

STAGE FIVE

(the upward turn)

the outside world

two weeks later my phone vibrated
incoming call from a nameless number

please, don't let it be the dopeman
i hope it's him, what's wrong with me?

hello? i answered cautiously

ahoy, matey!

Everett! greetings, earthling!
it's good to hear your voice

do i sound like a free man?

actually, you sound like shit

i'm gettin' over a cold, dick

i'm just playin', hope ya feel better

yeah, yeah, so what's goin' on?!
i see you haven't gotten a new number yet

i know, i'm gonna, just haven't gotten around to it
been busy relearning how to live sober...

plus, how would you have called me if i had?

what's your day count now? he asked

thirty-six!

daaamn, son, killin' it!

get a sponsor yet?

no, i said

better get on it
i didn't get one either the first time
and we both know how that worked out...

i'm not tryin' to give you shit, man
just lookin' out for ya

i know, i know...

i appreciate it, i said

found some good meetings, though
and i've been workin' out a lot
work's been crazy, but fine
livin' with Dev has been great
he even stopped keepin' alcohol in the house...

but still, i know what you mean now
about it bein' much different without those walls

right? but that's great, man, Everett said
i'm happy for ya

thanks...

so how are you?! i asked

other than this cold, pretty good
got out a few days ago...

by the way, shit sucked once you left...

but yeah, i'm good, man
gettin' settled in at the three-quarter house
definitely a huge adjustment...

some weird-ass dudes up in here

but i'm glad to be in Cleveland...

oh shit, dude, i almost forgot
you remember Mallory?

yeah, of course, what about her? i asked
scanning through the mental pics i'd snapped in rehab

man, she was beautiful, i think, or maybe even say out loud

she OD'd and died, Everett said

wait, what?

yeah, man

the fuck?

i know...

it's easy to forget what's at stake here...

and Trent, from our table? he asked

no

same thing...

you there? he asked

fuck, man

i know, he was only nineteen...

same thing happened after i got out the first time
people's tolerances are low and they go back out
do the same amount they did before, and that's it...

this shit's no joke

i better get that sponsor

yeah, bro, that new number too
last thing you want is the dopeboy hittin' you up...

you still got this, though, he said
sounds like you're doin' all the right things
except gettin' a sponsor and changin' your number, that is...

it takes time, i get it
but don't wait too long, Cam

i won't, i said

love ya, boss, he said

love you too

i still got this

like Everett said

but his wasn't the only voice

in my head

a merciless predator was lurking

the unnerving cacophony of sound

ominous prophecies
a monstrous constancy

legions of demons
vying for my allegiance
strategic and exact in their offense
masterfully hidden traps in each synapse
every thought a risk
a slaughterous attack from within
civil-warrish horror
Four Horsemen ready
the end is near

the vicious battle rages
the opposition flanking
easily overtaking my scattered defenses
insistent on surrender
resistance seems deadly

but so does giving in

i still got this?

feelings check-in

Cameron, is something bothering you?

i hate small meetings

would you like to share with the group?

not really, i mutter

*we're not here to judge or condemn you, just to listen
and remember*—you're only as sick as your secrets

i thought these meetings were anonymous

pass, i say

*okay, we can come back to you later
if you want to share then, great
if not, that's okay too
just keep coming back*

fine, you wanna know how i feel? i ask, standing up

naked, exposed

i feel like i'll never be able to stay sober...

hopeless, broken

i feel like i can't do this anymore...

what's the point?

*i feel like i wanna get blackout drunk
and see how many pills i can stuff up my nose...*

and never wake up

i feel like i don't really know any of you
and you don't know me...

i don't know myself

i feel like talkin' about it definitely *doesn't help*

how's that?

thanks for sharing, Cameron
keep coming back

instead of sitting down, i leave
let the door slam behind me
storm outside, category five
damn near rip car door off hinges
jump inside, yank it closed with a crash
sit in my car, in the parking lot
shaking, sweating, seething

fumble for my wallet
the cravings letter inside

unfold it frantically
read it once, then again
then a third and fourth time

read 'til i'm blind
'til the words lose all meaning

empty, i toss the paper aside

my gaze now on my faded jeans
the slightly raised outline of my phone

one thought
two thoughts
three thoughts
four

five thoughts
six thoughts
seven thoughts
more

milliseconds passing
heels tapping
thunder clapping
unprecedented force

legs in pain, still bouncing
burning flames, unblinking eyes
heart pounding razor blades
no more thinking, animal brain

fingers instinctively pouncing
plucking phone from pocket
punching numbers, hypnotic
contact deleted, not forgotten

breathing slows
eyes close

calm *after* the storm

ring

ring

ring

there isn't a fourth

old friends

he's not a drug dealer

he's my friend

i can't blame him

it's not his fault

what about the people he gets pills from?

what about the doctors?

the pharmaceutical companies?

it's all about the money

always and everywhere

they don't care if we live or die

they're all drug dealers

what a time to be alive

brainwashed

laminated hand-me-down readings
cliché phrases and formulaic prayers
holding hands, archaic folding chairs

forgive the cross talk, but are y'all in a cult?
what does it all mean?
are these robots breathing?

more meetings, more meetings
the same damn readings
the phrases and prayers
stale cake and éclairs

more meetings, more meetings
now i'm doing the readings
repeating the phrases
praying for serenity
saying the Our Father
sipping coffee-flavored water

more meetings, why bother?
can we do a different reading?
keep comin' back, comin' back, comin' back
i wanna attack the echo in the room
dude, why are your hands so sweaty?
no, i don't want another toffee
and this coffee sucks

eventually, i found a sponsor
asked what his thoughts were

he said, *Cameron, if you're like me...*

your brain needs *washing*

the twelve steps

step one [7]

i admit i'm powerless
over my addiction

my life is unmanageable

done with step one

step two's about believing
a Power greater than me
can make me clean

step three's about deciding
to trust this Power, this God
with my recovery, my life

i wanted to believe
and tried to decide
but couldn't seem to find
this Higher Power, this God

let alone trust

can i just skip to step four?

before we do that, this'll be fun
let's go back to step one

am i *really* powerless?

better yet, forget the steps for a sec

do i *really* need to keep comin' back?

who says? where's the evidence?

graveside

this 80's for you, i say

brown dirt fresh beneath my feet

flowers rest on the headstone sleek

the second date still blank

let's beatbox before we go in, i hear him say

then driving away, into the night

who's got the light?

you got it now, bro

lemme know how it is

sick o' this artificial shit

look what it did to you, dammit

but here i sit, your name in granite

waiting for the 80s to take me away...

rest in peace, Cheese Face

detention

i will not use tomorrow
i will not use tomorrow
i will not use tomorrow
i will not use tomorrow
i will not use tomorrow
i will not use tomorrow
i will not use tomorrow
i will not use tomorrow
i will not use tomorrow
i will not use tomorrow
i will not use tomorrow
i will not use tomorrow
i will not use tomorrow
i will not use tomorrow
i will not use tomorrow
i will not use tomorrow
i will not use tomorrow
i will not use tomorrow
i will not use tomorrow
i will not use tomorrow
i will not use tomorrow
i will not use tomorrow
i will not use tomorrow
i will not use tomorrow
i will not use tomorrow
i will not use tomorrow
i will not use tomorrow
i will not use tomorrow
i will not use tomorrow
i will not use tomorrow
i will not use tomorrow
i will not use tomorrow

i will not use tomorrow
i will not use tomorrow
i will not use tomorrow
i will not use tomorrow
i will not use tomorrow
i will not use tomorrow
i will not use tomorrow
i will not use tomorrow
i will not use tomorrow
i will not use tomorrow
i will not use tomorrow
i will not use tomorrow
i will not use tomorrow
i will not use tomorrow
i will not use tomorrow
i will not use tomorrow
i will not use tomorrow
i will not use tomorrow
i will not use tomorrow
i will not use tomorrow
i will not use tomorrow
i will not use tomorrow
i will not use tomorrow
i will not use tomorrow
i will not use tomorrow
i will not use tomorrow
i will not use tomorrow
i will not use tomorrow
i will not use tomorrow
i will not use tomorrow
i will not use tomorrow
i will not use tomorrow

i will not use tomorrow
i will not use tomorrow
i will not use tomorrow
i will not use tomorrow
i will not use tomorrow
i will not use tomorrow
i will not use tomorrow
i will not use tomorrow
i will not use tomorrow
i will not use tomorrow
i will not use tomorrow
i will not use tomorrow
i will not use tomorrow
i will not use tomorrow
i will not use tomorrow
i will not use tomorrow
i will not use tomorrow
i will not use tomorrow
i will not use tomorrow
i will not use tomorrow
i will not use tomorrow
i will not use tomorrow
i will not use tomorrow
i will not use tomorrow
i will not use tomorrow
i will not use tomorrow
i will not use tomorrow
i will not use tomorrow
i will not use tomorrow
i will not use tomorrow

i will not use tomorrow
i will not use tomorrow
i will not use tomorrow
i will not use tomorrow
i will not use tomorrow
i will not use tomorrow
i will not use tomorrow
i will not use tomorrow
i will not use tomorrow
i will not use tomorrow
i will not use tomorrow
i will not use tomorrow
i will not use tomorrow
i will not use tomorrow
i will not use tomorrow
i will not use tomorrow
i will not use tomorrow
i will not use tomorrow
i will not use tomorrow
i will not use tomorrow
i will not use tomorrow
i will not use tomorrow
i will not use tomorrow
i will not use tomorrow
i will not use tomorrow
i will not use tomorrow
i will not use tomorrow
i will not use tomorrow
i will not use tomorrow
i will not use tomorrow

you know what they say

about tomorrow

but then one day, i met Rachel

one of those friend of a friend things

we started messaging on Facebook

then texting

calling

FaceTiming

i was halfway in love

before our first date

can you say *good timing?*

the first letter i sent

Hey, Rachel!

For starters, I want to reiterate how much I've enjoyed getting to know you over the past several weeks. In the spirit of continuing to get to know each other, there's something I want to tell you that I think you should know about me. It's not something that's easy for me to talk about, but at the same time it's a big part of my life and is something I feel inclined to lay out on the table now—as opposed to sidestepping the issue, only to have it surface later and undermine any sort of trust we've established between us.

I've struggled with drug and alcohol abuse for basically the last eleven years of my life. I won't go into all the details here, but I'll do my best to tell you a little bit about where I've been and where I am today.

Virtually from the start, I felt conflicted. I will admit that it was fun for a while, and it even seemed sort of innocent at times, at least in the beginning, but these notions quickly faded. I knew deep down that I was on a dangerous path, but I constantly rationalized my behavior and told myself I would stop at such and such a date, but that date came and went time and again.

Although my life looked fine from the outside, at least from a distance, on the inside I was a complete mess. Yet, it was easy for me to hide behind my résumé and deny to myself and others that there was a problem. While I may have fooled others for a time, I couldn't fool myself. I knew there was a problem, a serious problem, but I couldn't accept that I wasn't the solution. My pride told me that I got myself into this mess, I can get myself out of it too, by my own strength and willpower. But despite my most sincere resolutions and desperate attempts to make changes in my life, nothing changed.

And then one day in January of this year, my mom and I were having breakfast before I went back to Cincinnati. (I had been home in Canton for the holidays.) As soon as we sat down to eat, she asked, *What the hell's going on with you?* My family had noticed the signs many times before, but I always brushed aside their concerns, saying that everything was fine and telling them not to worry. There was something different about the way my mom asked the question this time, though. I don't know what it was, but I had a strong suspicion she wasn't going to be satisfied with my typical bullshit response.

I opened my mouth to answer, figuring I'd give her a little more of the truth than I usually did, but not enough to worry her. Once I started talking, though, I couldn't stop. The words just came pouring out. (Dev had written me this letter a few months before that must have shaken something loose inside, but I can tell you more about that another time.) I don't even remember what I said exactly. I do remember the look on my mom's face, though, as she listened in silence. When I was done talking, she said, *It feels like I got hit by a freight train.*

A week after my mom confronted me, I was checking into rehab. Detox wasn't fun, but once everything was out of my system, I was able to think clearly for the first time in years. It was as if a veil had been lifted. I was able to look people in the eye again, and to look at myself in the mirror without hating the person staring back. I was discharged after twenty-one days, at which time I returned to Cincinnati, moved into a new apartment with Dev (where I live now), and returned to work a week later.

I can't explain how grateful I am that my mom confronted me when she did. I can hardly imagine the strength and courage that required, and how painfully difficult it had to have been for her and my dad to hear the ugly truth of what my life had become, and yet, through the tears, to tell me they love me and would do anything and everything they could to help me. I can't explain how grateful I am that Dev wrote me that letter. (I'll just have to show it to you sometime because me trying to describe it won't do it justice.) I'm also grateful for the tremendous amount of prayers, love, and support I've received from my family and friends through all of this. But I'm especially grateful for God's protection through it all; it's a miracle I'm still alive today.

It hasn't been an easy road, and I'm not "fixed" by any means. I have a long journey ahead of me, and although it seems a dreadfully slow and incredibly difficult process at times, I'm learning to be patient. I'm so thankful for the second chance I've been given, and I'm even thankful for what I've been through, because if things hadn't gotten so bad I don't know if I would have ever learned the things I'm learning today. I'm far from perfect (obviously) and still have a lot to learn, but I guess what I'm trying to say is that I've begun walking the road to recovery.

I'll conclude by saying I hope all of this doesn't scare you off. It's just such a big part of my story that I wanted to be up-front and honest with you about it. I hope I was clear and that what I wrote makes sense. If you have any questions, please don't hesitate to ask; I won't be offended or annoyed or anything like that. I'm used to all sorts of reactions from people, so don't feel like there's a "right" way to respond or worry about saying the "right" thing.

Sincerely,
Cameron

my twenty-seventh birthday

8:19 a.m.

it's so nice to be on a new path this year

every recent birthday was supposed to be the one i got sober

i've had some setbacks, but i'm really doing it this time

today is day eleven!

this is the longest i've been sober since the first time i relapsed

life is g double-o d good

8:27 p.m.

so much for a new path this year

went to a meeting i hadn't been to before
only four cars in the parking lot, five including mine

i hate small meetings

tiptoed up the stairs, following the signs
got to the top, looked right, left, straight ahead
all the doors were closed, so i bolted

got into my car, knowing it was a bad idea
started driving, clenched fists, vise grip

wouldn't be expected home for over an hour
Dev was at a work happy hour, so i prob'ly had even longer
driving onward, senses heightened, hyperaware

i could stop at the grocery store for a bottle
don't wanna see anyone i know
better go to a liquor store instead

just go home

i have to go

no, you don't

liquor store on the left

call your sponsor

no

think about this

jerk wheel into turn lane
pull into parking lot
take first spot
car off
jog

can i help you find something? the clerk asks

you got half-pints of whiskey back there?

we got Jack, Maker's, Crown, Jameson, Jim Beam

Jim Beam, please, i say

back in the car, looking at the bottle
holding it with both hands
twisting cap off, back on
thinking about Rachel

what if she asks how long i've been sober?

she won't

thinking about my family, my friends

what friends?

bottle in my hand

no turning back now

took a swig, then another
now i'm driving again

just go home

drove to a bar instead
already drank, might as well *drink*
finished the bottle, went inside

now i'm having a beer at the bar, in the corner, alone
trying to decide when to leave to guarantee beating Dev home

half an hour should be fine

plenty of time

aaaaand Rachel just texted me back

i had texted her before the "meeting"
she'll prob'ly ask how it went, what i'm doing
scared to check

can i have another beer, please? i ask

what did i just do?

make it two

was it worth it?

and a shot

eleven days gone

make it a double

back to day one

i'm gonna blow it with Rachel, dammit, she just texted again

look at all these fucking people—happy, laughing, i hate them all

no, Everett, i've never once drank or did drugs responsibly, okay?!

can i have a six-pack to go? i ask the barkeep

happy fucking birthday, Cam, you piece o' shit

are you even capable of thinking about anyone but yourself?

the chase

i never lost faith
expectations high
each and every time
this time'll be different
not a doubt in my mind
i've figured it out—
two lines of this
two hits of that
three sips, homie
going, going, *gone*

magic in my eyes
hope?
nope
eyes glazed from the dope
i won't give up
i'll figure it out
without a doubt
tonight's the night
i've got it now—
three lines of this
one hit of that
two sips, homie
going, going, *gone*

just like it was
a long time ago
when i didn't know
what i do now
shit, it's gone
fizzled out
next time i'll get it right
not a doubt in my mind

this time's the one

togetherness
understanding
love

yup, it's a vibe—
four lines of this
zero hits of that
one sip, homie
going, going, *gone*

alienation
misinterpretation
hatred

used to be so easy
why's it such a fight?
will i ever get it right?

*this very night
just wait and see
how easy it can be*

will i ever find what i'm looking for?

*that and more, surely
around the corner
have some faith*

all i have is the chase

awakening

8:48 a.m.

day four clean and sober

yesterday i told my parents about the continued relapses

through tears, my dad said he wanted me to live a long, happy life

please, step up and get this right
please, please, please, do whatever you need to do to stay sober

my mom was in shock, didn't say much
texted this morning saying she woke up crying
in the middle of the night, could barely breathe
the weight of it all, waiting for the call
saying i was dead, in jail, God knows what else

holy shit, i don't wanna go through that again

you?! what about them?!

it's like i forget

i wish there was a way to keep this fresh
short of relapsing, that is

i'm killing them—my parents, Dev

were our efforts in vain?
after everything we've done, how could you do this again?
are you even trying?

if you don't want to do it for yourself
at least have the decency to do it for us

i'm sorry, i do want this, it's just…

even i don't believe a word i say

epiphany

i play the innocent victim

and yeah, it's a disease

but i'm at least partially to blame

i may have set the aforementioned mental traps myself

unintentional, self-betraying, traitorous help

ignorant teenage choices and behaviors

create neural pathways

riddled with danger

one hit, sip, pill, line, dose, cap, stem at a time

paving the way to my own grave

bricks and land mines

yo, *i'm* the enemy

drugs aren't the problem, but a symptom

i'm the problem

and a victim

confusion

hello?

i have to tell you something, i said

Cam?

yeah

*i thought so, just didn't recognize the number
how the hell are ya, broski?!*

finally changed it, i mumbled

you okay? Everett asked

ughhhhh

what's wrong?

i...

yeah?

i relapsed

what happened?

i don't even know

*yeah, dude, totally understand that
it's only a date anyway
was it back on pills?*

yeah, drinkin' too

how long?

i don't know, man, off and on since last time we talked...

doin' better now, though, i said

all that matters is your attitude, man
glad you're positive about it...

have you told your family? Everett asked

yeah

what about Rachel?

no

you should tell her, he said

i wanna wait 'til i have more time, like a respectable amount...

can't be like—i really wanna stay sober
but i've been relapsing...

long story short, i have seven days clean
will you marry me?

Everett laughed

i've told her about my struggles, i said
just haven't explicitly told her i've relapsed...

we haven't even been talkin' that long...

i haven't lied, she just hasn't asked how long i've been sober

you don't have to justify yourself to me, man, i get it...

all i'm sayin' is she might see things differently, he said

whaddayou mean? i asked

well, when i relapsed after the first rehab stint
the situation was a little different

my girlfriend knew right away
we were livin' together
couldn't really hide it

that's kinda how it is with me and Dev...

shit, sorry, man, go 'head

no, you're good, i was just sayin' i couldn't really hide it...

and she left because of it...

i'm not sayin' that's gonna happen with Rachel
but relapsing is a bigger deal than it feels like to us...

or maybe not relapsing so much as the lying...

but trust me, i get it, no judgment here
relapse is part of my story too...

it doesn't matter, the past is the past
all that matters is what you do now
and you're off to a good start
you've already told your family
now you're tellin' me

i'm gonna tell my sponsor too, next time we meet, i said

my man, Everett said
it's a good sign that you're talkin' about it
tellin' others means you wanna stop...

i know how hard it is, man, and i appreciate you tellin' me...

you got this, homie...

and do what you wanna do with Rachel
but for what it's worth, i think you should tell her
sooner than later, that's just me, though...

relapse in and of itself is almost to be expected
it's the lying about it that tends to cause trouble

ugh, i don't know what to do, i said
things have been goin' so good with her
she's movin' to Portland soon, or tryin' to at least
been a dream of hers for a while...

recently, things have started to fall into place
it sucks, but everyone else is tryin' to discourage her
so i've been encouraging her to follow her dreams...

whatever, we can still make it work...

we're already long distance, what's it matter
if it's a four-hour drive or two-thousand-some miles?
don't answer that...

i wanna wait and see what happens, though
and enjoy the rest of the time we have together...

i'll tell her, i will...

but not yet...

i don't even know what i'd say right now, i said

that's understandable, Everett said
take your time, man, and keep your head up
do what you gotta do...

if you don't stay sober it's likely over anyway

i know

i know you do, and you know i'm always here
i'll check in with you in a couple days
but feel free to hit me up in the meantime

for real, man, hit me up whenever

thanks, man, i said

no need to thank me, Everett said
you'd do the same for me...

you're gonna be fine
you got this...

i love ya, Cam

love you too, i said

the chase (continued)

misguided hope
seems to float
like the real thing
clinging to pride
waving hello to the lifeboat
sinking all the while
pretending to swim
a speck on the horizon
the island's a mirage
a collage of romanticized memories
heavily camouflaged, expertly disguised treachery
an ever-present elusiveness
i've done too many hallucinogens
does what i'm looking for even exist?

metaphors aside, can i go back to how things were before?

sometimes i wonder how life would've transpired
if i'd just said no that night
airtight-closed door

would i have said yes the next time?
or eventually, like, inevitably?

i was so young, i hadn't even become

how can i go back to how things were?

how can i return to what never was?

becoming

this time'll be different
not a doubt in my mind
i've figured it out—
zero lines of this
zero hits of that
zero sips
simple as that

it was never easy
it'll still be a fight
even more so now
but tonight's the night

i never lost faith
it was just misplaced
what i deemed "the chase"
was really me running away

it's time to be where my feet are
the beginning of a new race
take your marks
get set

stay

today, i will think every thought
and feel every feeling
even when it hurts the worst
i will learn to be me

and what it means

to be real [8]

progress, not perfection

my sponsor, Andy, kept saying

it works if you work it—*so keep working it!*
and whatever you do, don't drink or use

i'd stay sober a handful of days, then relapse
then come back, i always came back

Andy was always waiting with a smile

welcome back, Cameron, had enough yet? he'd ask

the man had been around a while
five years sober, three decades older
could've been my dad

you're lucky to be in the program so young, he would say

Andy seemed younger than his age
maybe because he was always laughing
which at first annoyed the shit outta me
like, what could possibly be so funny?

keep coming back, they'd say

i remember the day i asked him to be my sponsor

sometimes, you just gotta tell your brain to fuck off

i burst out laughing when he said that

walked up to him after the meeting

excuse me, Andy? my name's Cameron, will you be my sponsor?

absolutely, let's meet this week, he replied with a knowing smile
not missing a beat, like he'd been expecting me

one day on the way to a meeting, Andy said (yet again)

you're lucky to be in the program so young

i'd offered to drive
he nicknamed the ride
"the meeting before the meeting"

never hurts to double up, he said
you gonna buckle up?

i put my seat belt on

you still have your whole life ahead of you, he continued
and you haven't lost much, not yet, but trust me—
it's only a matter of time...

you'll lose everything if you keep drinking and using

yet that's exactly what i keep doing, i said

you don't have to keep living that way
and for the record, you're supposed to call me before *you pick up*

i know, i'm sorry

you don't have to be sorry
i appreciate you telling me now...

so what happened, Cameron?

i had just pulled into the church parking lot

i'll tell you after the meeting...

we're gonna be late

wanna get some real coffee? Andy asked after the meeting
taking his last sip of the "cat piss" (his words) served inside

how does an alcoholic not know how to make coffee?

why'd you finish it if it was so bad? i asked
i stopped drinkin' that crap months ago

alright, smart-ass, you ready to tell me what happened?

sure

i talked 'til my throat hurt
all the way to the coffee shop
while we walked in, ordered, found a seat

Andy just listened, sipping his drink

that's all i got, i finally said

i gulped my drink, set it back down on the table
forming the fifth and final Olympic ring of condensation

now i have to pee

three minutes later, i was back in my seat
Andy smiled, staring at me, waiting

what's so funny? i asked

that was a long pee

it's all this coffee, how have you not peed yet?

*also, i was just thinking how we're having a meeting
after the meeting,* after *the meeting,* he said, smiling wider

glad you were listening

you don't have to take everything so seriously, Cameron
of course, i was listening, and you know what i think?

what?

i think you're finally ready

for what?

to get serious about working your program

i thought you just said not to be so serious

there's a difference, smart-ass

that's the second time you've called me a smart-ass, old man

what's your point?

you gonna tell me what i should do?

what do you think you should do?

you keep sayin' i need to get through the steps
but i haven't finished two or three yet

yes, you have

how?

you believe people can get sober, right?

i guess

that's step two

but i don't know what this Higher Power is all about
i mean, i say God when i pray or whatever
but i don't know who or what that is

that's okay, as long as it's not you, he said
it can be anything you want it to be—
he, she, it, we, them, a friend
a sponsor (he winked when he said this)
the steps, the program, anything...

some say God, but i don't care what you call it
as long as it's not Cameron...

make sense?

i guess so, i said

good, step three is about surrendering
and being willing to do whatever it takes...

let's just say, for now, it looks like this—
talking to me, going to meetings, and doing the steps

sooooo, i'm done with steps two and three?

you're never really done with three...

it's daily, sometimes several times a day, a constant surrendering

okay

but yes, you're ready for step four if that's what you were really asking

i was afraid you were gonna say that

step four is scary, but it's liberating
when you write out all your junk on paper
then—step five—tell someone else what you wrote...

namely, me, Andy said with a smile

yeah, that's terrifying, i said, forcing a smile

more terrifying than going back out?

no, i admitted

well, alrighty then...

steps six and seven—character defects
you wanna get rid of them, right?

yeah

then eight and nine—making amends
which boils down to cleaning your side of the street
accepting responsibility and apologizing for what you've done
and, perhaps most importantly, forgiving yourself...

steps ten through twelve are ongoing
but let's focus on four through nine for now, Andy said

can you say 'em again? i asked

you have your book with you? [9]

yeah

well, get it out!

what page? i asked, grabbing it from my bag

here, give it to me

Andy flipped right to the page

read, he said, handing the book back to me

out loud? i asked

Andy just looked at me and nodded
as if to say, *obviously*

fine, i conceded, even though he hadn't said anything

i read steps four through nine out loud, then put the book down

crikey, i said

it sounds like a lot, Andy said
one step at a time, though...

if i can do it, so can you...

it doesn't have to be perfect

he read my mind

just keep it moving, and get through them, he continued
no matter how imperfect it is...

God will meet you where you are...

*you can go through the steps as many times
as your little heart desires...*

*it's encouraged to keep going through them the rest of your life
like peeling back layers of an onion...*

*however, before you can go through them twice
you have to get through them once...*

you damn hippie, Andy added with a laugh
when you gonna get a haircut?

you're just jealous, i said, laughing too
but no, seriously, this was helpful

it's helping me too, Cameron, so it's not entirely selfless

i see how it is, i said, smirking

smart-ass, Andy said, smirking back

gratitude

dude! guess what today is?! my ninety-day anniversary!

ahhh shit! hell yeah, man! Everett said
you doin' anything to celebrate?!

um, no, not really, hadn't thought about it

ninety days is a big deal—treat yo'self, fool!
but either way, that's awesome, man
congratulations, for real, he said

thanks, homie...

i don't know, man, it's felt different lately

how so? he asked

like, i'm actually starting to believe i can stay sober
and i want to, like really *want to, more than before*
and i'm holding myself more accountable, i guess...

okay, here's an example—i was tryin' to walk off a craving
some random Tuesday, and i'm walkin' like a madman
ended up passin' a liquor store, accidentally on purpose
ya know, and i decided to go inside, just to look around
like maybe they'd gotten some new drinks or whatever
somethin' stupid, and, of course, i bought a bottle
then walked around my neighborhood, brown baggin' it
and i was almost proud on some level that no one found out...

but now, if i go on a walk, i don't even bring my wallet...

so, it's better, i said

that's great, man, i'm happy for ya...

i can hear a difference in your voice even
you sound almost...

happy, Everett said

i wouldn't go that far
but today's a good day
and i wanted to let you know and say thank-you...

i wouldn't have made it without you, bro

i'm stoked i could help in some small way
but you're the one doin' the heavy lifting...

you should be proud of yourself, man...

but not too proud, because you still can't do this alone, Everett said

thanks, i said, laughing, *and touché...*

by the way, sorry i haven't been responding lately
i've been, uh, on a little break from my phone, i said

no need to apologize, although i was gettin' a little worried
so i'm happy to hear you're still alive
and that you're sober and things are good...

how's it goin' with Rachel?

you still there? Everett asked

yeah...

she's gone, i mumbled

come again?

she's gone, i repeated, louder this time

shit, man, what happened?

it's a long story, i said

i got time, unless you'd rather not talk about it

no, it's cool, it kinda helps actually
and Dev's sick of hearin' about it

i'm all ears, homie

welp, i'll just dive right in then...

i was plannin' on tellin' her about the relapses, like we talked about...

i wanted to tell her in person, though
and we only saw each other on weekends
so already had limited opportunities
and every time we were together was so fun
there was never a good time to bring it up
no awkward pauses in the conversation or anything...

i ended up not tellin' her 'til the last time we were together
a couple nights before she was leavin' for Portland...

we're at her house, her parents are gone
we're sittin' in the kitchen, talkin' about somethin'
i don't remember what, but it was as good of a segue as any...

didn't tell her all the details or anything
basically, i just told her i'd relapsed, ya know
a few times or whatever and here's my day count

and? Everett asked

it went surprisingly well
she was really cool and understanding
everything seemed fine...

i left shortly afterward, not thinkin' anything of it...

felt great to have told her, though

i bet, Everett said

the next couple days were normal
then she left...

she and her mom were drivin' out to Portland
she was sendin' pictures and stuff all day, callin' at night
everything still seemed fine...

then one day out of the blue she just stopped responding...

thought she got in a wreck or somethin'
didn't know what to think
couldn't get a hold of her
radio silence...

then like a week or two later she called and said
i had lied to her and she needed time to process...

told me not to reach out...

said she'd call when she was ready to talk

damn, Everett said

i did not *see that comin', so i start ramblin' on and on*
i don't even know what the hell i said...

ended up writin' her a letter
and yeah, haven't heard from her since
been about a month
nothin' at all...

but i'm tryin' to give her space
and it's hard and it sucks and how long does it take to process?

ughhhhh...

sorry, man, that was a lot, i said
prob'ly was all over the place too

you're good, bud, i appreciate the details, Everett said
and i'm really sorry...

however it shakes out, you're gonna be okay
when my girlfriend left, i was a mess for a while
but now i see it as a blessing almost

how? i asked

it woke me up i guess
next thing i knew, i was back in rehab
and here i am today, sober and life's good

how long you have now? i asked

almost seven months, mutha chucka!

congrats, man, that's awesome

but no, keep your head up, bro
you never know what's gonna happen...

i'm really proud of you, Cam
you told her and that's not easy
and you're still sober—ninety days sober!

thanks, Everett...

and, like you said, you never know...

i'm proud of you too, though, dude
seven freaking months, that's huge

i'm proud of us, he said
we're doin' it, man!

the second (and last) letter i sent

Dear Rachel,

I know you requested that the ball be in your court as far as the next communication goes, and I intend to honor your request. I won't reach out again; however, the reason for your silence as of late caught me off guard and I wanted to apologize for responding defensively, as well as for anything I said that suggested I take any of this lightly.

When I heard you say you feel deceived and your guard is up, my heart sank. My immediate reaction was to justify why I waited to tell you about relapsing. I now see that my reasons for waiting were nothing more than excuses. It was incredibly selfish and misleading of me to withhold that information from you, and I failed to fully realize the implications of doing so.

You're such an amazing person, Rachel. Everything you've been through; the things you've accomplished; the places you've been; the depth of your faith; and the overall sense of joy, peace, hope, and confidence that radiates from your presence made me wonder how on earth you'd be interested in someone like me if you knew the truth. So, I portrayed myself as being further along in my recovery than I was by not telling you the whole truth.

I've been a liar, manipulator, and people pleaser for as long as I can remember. I filter what others know about me to present myself in a positive light. I go into relationships with unspoken expectations, then harbor resentments when others fail to meet the unrealistic demands I've put on them without their knowledge. I make assumptions in relationships and proceed accordingly, even though my assumptions rarely align with reality. I'm selfish, self-centered, and self-seeking. Despite being sober today, these character defects are still more prevalent than I'd like to admit.

I should have told you about my relapses sooner. It makes me sick to think about the pain I've caused you, especially as you're in the process of beginning a new chapter in your life, not that it would have been any better if that weren't the case. I'm so sorry, Rachel.

I don't expect anything I've said to make you forget what happened or change the way you feel about it. You have every right to feel deceived, and I completely understand why you've withdrawn over the past few weeks. I can't stress how sorry I am, and I sincerely hope and pray you can forgive me. I also don't expect anything I've said to make you trust me again. I know you may never trust me again.

I'm not trying to overwhelm you with even more to think about by writing this letter. I am more than willing to discuss this further when you're ready, but take as much time as you need to process everything. In the meantime, I intend to focus on my recovery. I'm happy to say I've made a lot of progress recently, and I'm fully committed to my continued sobriety.

Love,
Cameron

perspective

which me will it be today?
your guess is as good as mine
did the pan fry the egg? or was my brain already fried?
am i clinically depressed? is medicine suggested?
scared to death to take a pill again, even with legit prescription
can i see a description of the grieving process? when's it end?
is this normal in recovery? am i doing something wrong?
it works if you work it—how can you tell if it's workin'?
all work and no play makes... [10]
half-baked thoughts, fragmented, disjointed
i never meant to be such a clusterfuck of a disappointment

still sober, though

how long will that last?
pass the gas and light a match
i can't naturally sustain this white-knuckle act
buckle the straitjacket snaps, i'm all over the map
more caffeine, nicotine, and chocolate chip cookies, please
goody gumdrops, the sun drops, and i can't sleep
can't stay in one place with these restless legs
prayin' for blessings and serenity obsessively
forgive my complaints but ain't tasted it yet
not even a lick—if i did, i forget
memory unclear, pickin' fights with mirrors
whatchu lookin' at, bitch? this anger, this fear
second guessin' everything, i'll never change
every day strange weather brings the explosion closer
supernova shit, i'm over it, can't wait to go bang

still clean, though

at least on the surface

the rain won't last forever, Cameron

my grandma said that to me one day
we were sitting on her porch swing
rocking slowly back and forth

without rain, there'd be no rainbows, and you know what else?
your old grandma's seen rainbows even when it hasn't rained…

God's finger-painted grace

she said that phrase with such delight
like a child might say *ice cream*
as if the words passing over her lips
were just as sweet a treat

that's what hope is all about, Cameron, and it's here, *right now*
just waiting for you to take hold of it…

go ahead, reach out your hands—here, like this, she said
lifting her arms up over her head

i did the same

and you know the best part? she asked, our arms still raised

what, Grandma?

whether you can see it or not
whether you take hold of it or not
even if the mountains fall into the sea… [11]

that hope is holding on to you, she said
touching my nose with her index finger

and to me

these days, i find myself sitting in bed

Grandma's voice in my head

my arms outstretched

r e a c h i n g

you doin' yoga? Dev asked
why are your arms up like that?

no, it's...

nothing, never mind, i said
when'd you get home?

just now, what are you up to?

oh, ya know, just mopin' around

you gotta get outta your head, man
and stop feeling sorry for yourself

Rachel's the one, man, i love her

you didn't even know her that long
maybe you fell in love, or maybe it's just infatuation...

you were fresh outta rehab, Cam

she coulda responded to the letter at least

maybe she will, but what's it gonna change?

do you think i shoulda told her about the relapses sooner?

honestly, i think you told her too *soon...*

oversharing is a real thing, he said

should i have waited to tell her about my past in general?

i don't know, man, relationships are confusing...

that might not have had anything to do with why she left...

we don't always get to know why things happen, Dev said

do you think things happen for a reason? i asked

i don't know...

but whatever happens, God can and does use it for good... [12]

you have a long journey ahead of you, bro
you need to focus on you for a while

all i seem to think about is myself, i said

i know it might be hard for you to see
but you've grown a lot over the past several months
i'm proud of you, Cam

ugh, why's it gotta be so hard?

i don't know, but you can do hard things
you're brave enough, strong enough, and disciplined enough
and at times you think you aren't, i'll be there...

i'm always here, Cam, and so is God

i was crying at this point

that sounds familiar, i said, sniffling
was that in the letter you wrote me?

maybe so, he said

this is your life, man! he continued
and there's a whole lotta livin' left for you to do
i don't know about you, but i don't wanna waste another second...

can't you see, Cam? we're alive! and sober!

i know, i said, *i just...*

don't know how to live

160

you're doin' great, Cam, just keep doin' what you're doin'...

and be patient—you don't have to do everything at once...

and it wouldn't hurt to try smiling occasionally...

just a thought, Dev said with a wink

i forced a smile

i appreciate the effort, he said

i don't know what i'd do without you, Dev

you'd be screwed, he said

i didn't have to force a smile that time

(more) progress, not perfection

i kept working the steps, like Andy said
taking them seriously, and myself less

learning to be patient, like Dev said
trying to at least, smiling more too

believe it or not, i'm starting to find
something that feels like freedom

finding God even

i think

i don't know

i don't understand most of it

whatever it is, i'm staying sober
which is all i need to know
can i get an *amen?!*

even though i haven't heard from Rachel yet

which brings us back to where we left off

her silence says enough

and rejection still sucks

but i got like six months sober now

somehow, someway

and life is good most days

STAGE SIX

(reconstruction)

'tis the season

I am so happy to spend the holidays with you, Cameron, and am very proud of all your accomplishments. I can only imagine the struggles you have had and maybe are still going through. You seem happier, but I think you may think sometimes that your life has not changed as much as you may have liked. But take heart, things have been getting better. You are excelling at work, and I am sure things will start clicking socially with meeting new friends, and that special girl. Your commitment to God will bring happiness to your life. You are a wonderful person, and I am so thankful and happy that you are my son.

I love you, Cameron, and Merry Christmas.
Dad

Wanted to let you know how proud of you I am for working so hard to reach this incredible milestone—six months of sobriety! It's wonderful to be able to celebrate that, and the courage and dedication you've shown while choosing each day to be clean. It's been really cool to see your growth over the past several months. You're showing up every day and doing hard things! You continue to inspire me, Cameron. You make me want to be a better person. I can't even imagine a life that you weren't in.

I hope this year brings you so much joy. There are no limits to what God has in store for you. I feel so blessed to have a front-row seat to watch you continue to grow and soar. I hope that you wake up every morning knowing just how loved you are. I'm so incredibly proud of you. Be super-duper proud of yourself, and live each day with joyful anticipation of what is certainly ahead for you.

With all my love,
Mom

no card from Rachel

not that i expected one

not even a text

a text woulda been nice

nothing

so, i wrote her a letter

that i never sent

remember that?

speaking of seasons

since leaving rehab—

spring sprung

summer summed

fall fell

winter sucks

scatter-brained, sometime in January

Everett relapsed.

Called me today. 9:30 a.m.

Already working on a six-pack.

Just like that.

People from my hometown keep dying. "People" sounds so vague, so foreign. I grew up with these people, went to school with them, walked by them in the halls. A lot of them were my friends. Acquaintances at the least. I know their names, their faces, their voices. I know where they worked and who they dated. I know their families.

Overdoses. Car accidents. Others are staying alive but ending up in jail, which arguably is a form of dying too. Some as young as eighteen, nineteen years old. Like, *what?!*

Feels like every month it's someone else. What's worse is that it doesn't even phase me anymore.

Here I am, alive and sober. By the grace of God. But what does that mean? Dev always says it's a miracle, and that you can't explain miracles. There has to be some kind of explanation, though, right? Like, how did I get here? Why me?

And there are others; walk into any recovery meeting (and they're everywhere), and you'll see entire groups of people staying clean and sober.

Why do some people get sober and others don't?

Why do some people die and others don't?

It's not just my hometown. Not just where I live now. It's universal. A pandemic. We're all addicted to something. Some addictions are just more visible and destructive than others. But what can you do?

There's nothing you can say to "fix" people. I can't explain to someone in active addiction what exactly I did that worked for me, how I went from where I was to where I am now. I could list off some things that helped and are helping currently, but they're just words.

It's more than just a list of dos and don'ts. There's a spiritual component to recovery. But that takes time, which can be problematic for addicts; any day could be their last. If you want to expedite the process, I suppose you could try beating someone over the head with your spirituality. Besides being annoying, that doesn't seem likely to produce the desired result either.

There has to be something you can do, though, right? If Dev hadn't written that letter and my mom hadn't staged a solo intervention of sorts, and if everything else that happened hadn't happened or had happened differently, who knows where I'd be today or if I'd even still *be* at all.

I don't have to wait until I have it all figured out. I think about some of the people who have helped me, and they're perhaps some of the most broken people I know. They've been through the ringer. They aren't perfect. Nobody is. Nobody has all the answers.

So maybe it's just about reaching out, showing up, and being there for someone. Coming as you are and meeting them where they are. Loving them through it all. But how do you love them without enabling them? How do you keep loving someone who treats you like shit? What if it seems like they aren't even trying or don't even want help?

It's so easy to forget there's a broken person beneath the surface who feels utterly trapped and is desperate for relief. They likely want to stop drinking and/or doing drugs more so than anyone else wants them to. They're aware of their behavior, the insanity of it all, and probably hate it more than you do. There's a strong chance they hate themselves too. This is a disease, and we're powerless over our addiction. And you're not God either.

Even for me it's easy to forget, and I was that person. I still am in some ways. And I try to play God too. I do have a part to play (and so do you), but it's not the latter.

Full disclosure, though—helping other addicts/alcoholics scares the shit out of me. It's much easier to watch from a safe distance, or to turn a blind eye altogether. To just focus on me and my little world. But what does that change? Who does that help? I can't just pretend this isn't happening. This is a serious problem, and I want to be part of the solution. But what the hell is the solution?

Relapse can happen to anyone. Even though I have close to seven months now, I'm still scared of relapsing. It doesn't matter how much clean time you have. Look at Everett. I'm not immune by any means. I never will be.

If I relapse again, I won't make it back. Getting clean and staying clean for this long is the hardest thing I've ever done, and I don't think I could do it again. That fear keeps me clean, among a multitude of other things. I've gotten through some hard things in recovery, as well as some lesser things that don't seem like big deals but are still significant, like weddings and holidays.

Who knows what's going to happen next, though? And it doesn't even have to be a big thing. A few months after I got out of rehab, I remember not being able to close the drawer beneath the oven. A pan had fallen out and was jammed in the back, but I didn't know that at the time, so I tried and tried to get the drawer to close and eventually sat down on the kitchen floor and cried. *I want fucking drugs!* I screamed through the tears. I wanted to get high then more so than when some of the "bigger" things were happening. Not to say the big things are easier, but that even a little thing can be the culprit. There are so many things that can happen in life. And the craziest thing is—nothing has to happen at all. It's terrifying.

And yet, the more time that passes, the more confidence I have. I'll be fine as long as I remember where I was, how far I've come, where I want to go, why I want to stay clean, and that I can't do this alone. So many things to remember, and I forget so easily.

You never think it can happen to you. I was convinced I would never overdose and die or get in a wreck or end up in jail or whatever. I would have argued with you about it if you thought otherwise. By the grace of God none of those things happened, but they certainly could have. They happen all the time. It can happen to anyone.

Even with pills. I never thought I could OD from pills, but today people press them with heroin, fentanyl, God knows what else. You never know what you're getting, even though you tend to think you do with pills. It's scary. And shit, I've done heroin and fentanyl before knowingly.

I know a guy who sold his mom the heroin that killed her. I know a girl whose two roommates in a halfway house decided to get high one last time and both died the same night. I know someone who used to search the local obituaries for people who died from cancer, then break into their homes during the funeral and steal their pain pills. That someone was me.

Such a seemingly hopeless situation all around. So many people—gone too early, and for what? So many people trapped in active addiction and alcoholism. It's heartbreaking. And yet, simultaneously, I don't feel a thing.

Or maybe I feel too much and shut down as a result. Like a self-protection thing. Either way, the numbness scares me.

I don't know what to do. I don't know what I *can* do.

I feel helpless.

God help us.

i digress

back to Everett
my best rehab friend

feels like i've known him forever
one of my "solids" for sure

that's what my rehab roommate used to call 'em
not the snorer in detox, but another guy
his name's James

Cam, there's a lotta people here 'cause they have to be
they ain't takin' it serious...

all of 'em gonna end up right back in here
or worse—they gonna end up dead or locked up...

bruh, you gotta find people that's goin' where you wanna go
and i know that ain't them places i said...

ain't nobody trust an old crackhead like James
but believe me, bruh, i know from experience...

bein' clean is easy in here, you ain't got a choice
but if you tryna stay sober, once you back on the outside
you gotta find your solids, and stick with 'em, my man...

pride gonna lie to you, make you think you don't need people
soon as you start believin' them lies, the enemy's already won...

you gotta keep your eyes on the truth
my Lord and Savior, Jesus Christ, he's the only way...

Jesus gotta be your number one solid

i digress, again
back to Everett
my best rehab friend

haven't seen him since
we live four hours away

but knowing he's out there
going through what i am
that i'm not alone

it's enough

and he relapses

just like that

this God-forsaken disease
no immunity, no vaccine

you're still in the fight
Everett, you gotta be

my best friend now

omit the "rehab" qualifier
no adjective, no disclaimer required

we would've been friends anyway
magnetic, atomic, a common thread

rehab or not

the only friend i've got
other than Dev

i never had a lot

i digress, again and again
back to Everett, my best friend

i checked in a few days later
he seemed positive, confident
had a plan to get back on track

it's like you said when i relapsed—
all that matters is your attitude
and what you do now, i said

the past is the past
you got this, Everett

said i'd keep checking in

felt good to be there for someone else
usually it's me on the receiving end
felt good to give, even a little bit

Andy would be proud

you got this, Everett...

we both do

keep your head up, man
do what you gotta do...

you're gonna be fine...

we both are

i'm always here, whatever you need...

i love ya, bro

you too, he said

i wonder

if i knew the last time was the last time

would i have done anything differently?

hope

i keep thinkin' about Rachel...

feels like she just left yesterday...

and also a lifetime ago

here we go again, Dev said
let her go, man, it's over

gee, thanks, didn't think of that

well, whaddayou wanna hear?
it's time to move on, man

i just...

miss having someone

you have me, he said

it's not the same

God sees you, Cam, and he knows
you just gotta trust his timing

any day now would be great, i said

hope that is seen is no hope at all [13]

what's that mean?

Dev just looked at me and smiled
those all-knowing, all-seeing blue eyes

confidence personified

god, i envied that

i wonder if

i knew the last time was the last time

could i have done anything differently?

(another) silent night

all is calm

all is bright

all upon a winter's night

lying on the couch
Dev sprawled out on the floor
watching a movie we've seen before

The Darjeeling Limited, our favorite—

these three brothers
who'd grown apart
reunite to embark
on what turns out to be
a spiritual journey of sorts

nothing goes as planned but it works out
arguably much better than expected

they even become friends in the end

i hope this movie never ends, i say

all is calm and bright again

all upon a winter's night

i wonder if i knew

the last time was the last time

should i have done anything differently?

STAGE SEVEN

(acceptance)

back in the beginning

it was fun
carefree
innocent
safe

or so it seemed

my friends and i
wild and free
expanding our minds
learning to be

addicted, even then

we were young

the invincible ones

i once was blind
but now i see

then, in the middle

it was (mostly) fun
(sometimes) carefree
(not as) innocent
still safe

it was all a dream

my friends and i

ignoring the signs

we knew what was what
had it all figured out
not a doubt in our minds

how could we have known?

we were still so young

wide-eyed and alive

i once was blind
but now i see

finally, in the end

it was Valentine's Day

last-minute lovers
waiting in line
buying flowers, cards, chocolate hearts
i blend right in
card in my right hand
candy in my left

except

the card is for Everett's family
the candy for me

Everett—

my best friend

my brother

he—

he died

last night

OD'd

vague obituaries

just say it

people that young
don't just die

he was only twenty-nine

JUST FUCKING SAY IT

we all know why

then again—

m
a
y
b
e

it's better

left unsaid

then again—

m
a
y
b
e

not

rest in peace

reach in pocket
handful of 30s
watch them dance across table
dirty glass, still smudged and dusty
surely a choreographed routine, it must be

pick up credit card, creased in middle
curtain closes, what a performance, i'm tickled
pills bowing, curtseying, crumbling to pieces
thanking me, the audience
for being so kind

well done, my friends, i applaud you

forming orderly lines

now come inside

nostril flared, invitingly
sniffing swiftly, mightily
devouring powder, lint, eyelashes
big chunks of pills
nothing missed

table clean

what a performance

but me—

no longer

close my eyes, darkness then light
open them slowly, mindfully
the high rising, rising
lean back, gliding
stare at ceiling, still peeling

here in this room again
heaven, hell, and purgatory
wrapped up in one

all of a sudden, ceiling shudders
plaster rolls up like a scroll
roof splits open, Red Sea-style [14]
bright blue sky, calling me home

rising, rising, higher still
soaring, flying
almost there

arms raised
reaching out

there now

a brilliant light

welcoming, enveloping, absolving, dissolving me

i'm surrendering, becoming the light

this must be what dying's like

the light

goes black

i'm

f

a

l

l

i

n

g

then

nothing

wake up
　　sweating
　　　　wanting
　　　　something
　　　　anything
　　　　everything
　　　　can't stay awake
　　　　can't fall back asleep
　　　　can't go on like this
　　　　chasing the wind
　　　　too many feelings
　　　　overload
　　　　shut down
　　　　waste away
　　　　disintegrate

　　　　i feel nothing again

　　　　after a while
　　　　pain loses its hurt
　　　　eventually numbness
　　　　hurts even worse

　　　　contemplate how to stop it

　　　　i know! grab a pill and pop it

　　　　no
　　　　stop it
　　　　won't go there again
　　　　never again
　　　　won't make anything better
　　　　never did
　　　　one day at a time
　　　　things'll get better again—　　　　　　right?

after a while

pain loses its hurt

eventually numbness

hurts even worse

then you die

he's in a better place, everyone keeps saying

how do they know?

there's a reason for his death, they say

i wish

i wish i could shove their worthless words back down their throats

next thing i know, i'm saying the same

he's finally at rest

he will live on

but he's gone

these absurd and worthless words

i know they're trying to help, as am i

we all wanna help when someone dies

so we lie to ourselves

what else can we do?

so many lies

where's the truth?

here's some—i wish my friends would stop dying

and i wish i could get high

i mean, i *could* get high

know i shouldn't, can't seem to remember why

don't even really want to, do but i don't

seesaw, teeter-totter, tightrope

feels more like a primal need

than a conscious choice

the voices screaming

hi, folks, thanks for tuning in
we're live inside Cam's mind, where the debate is underway...

should he get high or not? the only question on the slate
proponents of both sides making rather convincing claims
you can feel the contentious energy in the air, folks...

Cam's attempting to be fair and weigh the arguments objectively
before he makes his ultimate decision...

let's have a listen—

just for today
just one more time
close your eyes

i see the little blue pill
the letter *M* inside a box imprinted on one side
the number 30 on the other
then another and another
covered by a credit card, one by one
feel them breaking apart beneath my thumb
see the line, feel the straw in my hand
the powder shooting up my nose
eyes open now
the eye-widening, coming-alive-again burn
head tilting back
gentle exhale from the mouth
none of the powder falls out
another big sniff with one nostril pinched
to get the rest of it down my throat

the sweet and subtle drip

no one's gonna know, go 'head
turn this hell into heaven in fifteen seconds
it'll be our little secret

so tired of the lies, the secrets

everything's a lie

don't know what to believe anymore

before you were even born, i was...

i'm the first, the last, but never second
the future, the past, the eternal present...

you will know the truth
and the truth will set you free...

the people walking in darkness
have seen a great light...

the light shines in the darkness
and the darkness has not overcome it [15]

where are you now?

i don't see any light
only darkness pretending
lonely darkness unending

stop wasting time, don't listen to him
you know you'll give in, just do it already
this is the only way to save
a wretch like you

i am a wretch, but i can't let everyone down again
it's the same every time, only gets worse
never think i can go any lower, but seem to know no rock bottom
always lower, bottom's always further down
no matter how far i've climbed

this time'll be different

no, it won't
well, i don't know
maybe it will

yes, it will

i want him back
still can't believe he's gone
but i can't go back

oh, relax, you'll be fine
what's one more time gonna do?

what if i die too?

good, that's it, play the tape through
take two seconds to breathe...

this too shall pass, eventually

there has to be another way

eventually's too long...

why wait?

Four Horsemen ready

the end is near

roll credits

fade to black

the end is here

it can't end like this

i better call my sponsor

Andy? how's it goin'? the voices are gettin' loud, man

i'm glad you called me
what's going on?

it's Everett, he...

passed away, i said

i'm sorry, Cameron, that's horrible...

are you up for getting together?
i'll be off work in an hour

sure

let's meet at the usual spot, and try to keep busy in the meantime
don't just sit there letting your brain run with this

i've already told my brain to fuck off like a million times, i said
trying to laugh but it sounded more like a grunt

attaboy, i'll see you soon, Cameron
and one more thing...

i've had a few sponsees over the years
who went back out and didn't make it back...

at first i blamed myself—why couldn't i save them?
but i've learned that's a burden i'm not meant to carry
i'm not God, i can't save anyone...

all that to say—don't blame yourself for what happened...

there's nothing you could have done...

it's not your fault, Cameron

an hour later, at our usual spot

ahh, Andy exhaled after taking a sip of his coffee

so, what are you gonna do? he asked, setting his cup down

what can i do? i mailed his family a card

i meant what are you gonna do to stay sober?
no one can change what happened
and it's gonna hurt for a while, a long while
but you still have a choice, Cameron
you worked hard for that choice...

if you pick up again, you will lose that power to choose

i gulped my coffee

i don't wanna use, but i also don't wanna feel the way i do
it's just one thing after another, man, this whole last year
ever since i got outta rehab...

i'm exhausted, man, i said

but you're doing it, buddy, one day at a time
stay in today, don't worry about tomorrow
going back out won't make anything better...

i was fifty-three when i got into the program, Andy said
you were what—twenty-six? twenty-seven?

twenty-six, i reminded him

can you imagine another twenty-seven years living how you were?
literally another lifetime for you...

you're lucky to have gotten into the program so young
to have gotten in at all…

you've been given an incredible gift, Cameron…

we only have today, and what you do today matters, immensely…

so i'll ask again—what are you gonna do, you damn hippie?

Andy smiled and i grunt-laughed

i don't know

well, you called me, which was a great first step
we can start getting together more frequently if you'd like
you should up your meetings too…

speaking of your program, Andy said
how are you coming along with your amends?

good, i'm pretty much done, i think…

one of the perks of bein' so young, i said, forcing a smile
my list wasn't that long

what am i always tellin' ya?!

amends are ongoing, though—living amends, that is…

it's one thing to say you're sorry
but in most cases, you've lost people's trust
you have to show them you're sorry, day in and day out…

steps ten through twelve are also ones you do every day
you're already doing them, most likely…

have you looked at ten through twelve yet? he asked

not really, but we always read 'em at the meetings

do you have your book with you?

no, i said

Andy opened his and began flipping through

i noticed all the handwriting, underlining, highlighting
all the dog-eared pages

he found the right one and passed the book to me

read, he said

by then, i didn't have to ask if he meant out loud

when i finished reading, i looked up at him

so, step ten is basically four and nine combined, in real time?
and eleven is working on my relationship with God?
then twelve is paying it forward, more or less?

in a nutshell, he said

i guess i kinda have been doin' those, tryin' to at least...

except twelve, i said

from what you've told me about Everett
it sounds like you've been doing twelve too...

plus, me and you getting together or talking on the phone counts
so does working the steps, living them out, going to meetings—
it's all part of it, buddy...

maybe you can get some sponsees of your own, someday
but for now, keep doing what you're doing, Cameron

ok, i said

semantics aside, you've come a long way since we first met give yourself some damn credit

a lotta the credit is yours, i said

i do accept thank-yous, particularly monetary ones...

you're helping me stay sober too, Cameron
just like i'm helping you...

even if we are just a couple bozos on the bus

thanks, Andy, i said, laughing, *for everything*

there it is! i've been waiting for that laugh...

keep smiling in the shitstorm, brother
and thanks for the coffee, he said

you're welcome, ya old bozo

in the end, it was Valentine's Day

bag of candy gone
card in the mail

can't remember what i wrote

it doesn't matter
there's nothing to say

these absurdly worthless words

will his family ever be okay again?

what about his friends?

what about me?

grief is

paralyzing shock, day after day
blinding pain, wave after wave
blame eating my insides like acid
more shock, indefensible
more pain, incomprehensible
always the blame, repeating decimals

now another wave of pain, the crest scrapes the sky
the wave crashes down, drowning me
it's like a dream, i can't die
floating in a pitch-black ocean, knowing
something's coming to get me from below
don't know what or when, hoping i wake up soon

a veil over my eyes, mummified
my face a bust, one expression unchanging, gathering dust
cold, soul-sucking smog, this wasteland haze
a minute holds a thousand days
time stopped in its tracks, looking back
wondering where the time went

looking back at the first three stanzas—
each is six lines of text, one space between
that's six six six, the mark of the beast [16]

all i wanna do is escape, close my eyes and sleep
but i can't even blink
the timeless silence screaming bloody murder
a legion of demons still competing for my allegiance
unheard-of, depths-of-hell darkness
weeping and gnashing of teeth [17]

another six lines of text for good measure
good grief, this shit is extra hellish

an unending maze
no way out
unpredictably repetitive

all these people going about their days
like everything's normal
don't they know?

everything's different
everything you see
the people
the streets
it's all the same
but it's not
not at all

a parallel universe
everything looks the same
except nothing is

never will be again

grief is not

forever

but might as well be

what can i do?

the void
the vacuum

black hole
pulling
ungluing
consuming

everything
that
makes
me
me

what's left?

a hollow-shelled nonentity

now *this*—

this *must* be

what dying's like

be that as it may

a remnant of life remains—

my broken heart, still beating

God's finger-painted grace

without rain, there'd be no rainbows

and you know what else?

your old grandma's seen rainbows

even when it hasn't rained

rain or shine

it's been a long time

since i've seen one

remembering

way back when, i slept through—

fire alarms
police car sirens
punches, kicks, and elbows
being straddled by girls i barely knew
getting arrested
etcetera

i slept through puking my guts and the drugs out
i slept through things i don't even know about

way back when, i woke up—

without my phone, wallet, or keys

handcuffed in a cop car

in hospital beds

naked in stranger's sheets
and even the front yard

with a needle in my arm

covered in blood

with broken bones

but no matter what i slept through
or where or when or how i woke up—

i always woke up (i.e., came to)

so many of my friends…they never…ughhhhh

Everett, i remember—

when we first met

playing Scrabble on my bed

spending the day outside
the first family visitation day
neither of our families came

we pretended we were each other's family
except it wasn't fantasy for long

when i left

the first time we talked once you got out

it was so good to hear your voice
i can still hear it now
the sound of your laugh

when i told you about relapsing
and about Rachel

you were always there
always knew what to say
and when not to say anything

my ninety-day anniversary
you said you were proud of me

your seven-month was coming up
i said i was proud of you

i'm proud of us, you'd said

i ended up gettin' a tattoo to celebrate
a portrait of your smiling face, right on my chest
a real work of art

i'm lyin', of course
that shit's already tattooed on my heart

dear Everett, i remember—

when you relapsed

the next several days, checking in

the last time we talked
you sounded better, sober again

music's my saving grace, you'd said
my band's back together, proper-like
we're playin' great, better than ever
even got some shows lined up

you were so excited, or at least *as* excited
as people in early recovery can be

you asked me if i was still writing
in rehab i'd let you read some poems of mine

damn, bro, you said after you read one
you should get this shit published!

i brushed it aside
no way, no how, forget it

you set the notebook down
put your hands on my shoulders
looked into and through my eyes
looked inside, i'd never felt so *seen*
completely paralyzed, transfixed by your gaze
naked, transparent, yet safe, unashamed
waiting for your reply

you let the silence speak

the silence thundered, teeming with substance

what are you waiting for? i wondered

it seemed you were waiting for me

i nodded my head yes, as if to suggest
i understand, i'm ready—proceed

maintaining your penetrating stare, oak-tree steady
you spoke, self-assured, words heavy in the air

not condescending or condemning
but a kind, compassionate plea

people are just people

why are you afraid?

our last conversation ended like the rest

i love ya, bro

love you too

i remember what happened next

how can i forget?

my best friend, my brother

my lesbian lover [18]

you'd said that one time
i laughed 'til i cried

still crying now

racking my brain

trying to explain, understand, make sense of this

never-ending run-on sentences

       leading

         nowhere

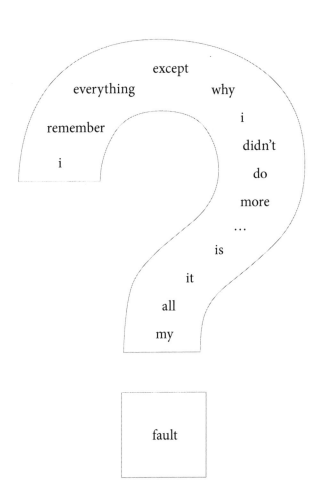

i
remember

everything
except

why

i
didn't
do
more
...

is

it

all

my

fault

endlessly wondering

if i knew the last time

was the last time

would i

could i

should i

have done anything differently?

people

why even try?

everyone i get close to leaves

or dies

pride gonna lie to you, James had said
make you think you don't need people

you say pride
i say i've tried

look where it's gotten me

Rachel left and Everett's dead

trying again isn't worth the risk

soon as you start believin' them lies
the enemy's already won

you say lies
i say real life

i don't need no help from people

i'm more than capable of hurting myself

you gotta keep your eyes on the truth

whatever, James

i'm better off

alone

what does he know anyway? he's a crackhead, remember?

James is my friend, one of my solids

where's he been? doesn't seem too solid to me
what's he or anyone else ever done for you?

i didn't get here on my own

everyone has their own motives for helping
even Andy said, it's not entirely selfless

that's not true, i mean, he said that, but that's not what he meant

if it came down to it—you or them—who would they choose?

cat got your tongue?

you're the only one you can trust
this is your life, Cameron, what do you want?

i'm thinking

you know the answer

i'm still so young

plenty of time to grow up, why not have some fun?

i...

what's one more time gonna do?

what if i...

you're not gonna die [19]

i'm...

c'mon, Cameron, while we're still young

home alone

snow on the ground

snow in the trees

TV sounds

the washing machine

watching *Friends* in bed

blanket up to my neck

phone battery red

i let it die

biding my time

waiting for spring to spring

waiting for something

always waiting

snow on the ground

snow in the trees

TV sounds

the dryer squeaks

are you still watching? appears on the screen [20]

i read, *have you showered today?*

i'm not taking questions right now

leave a message after the beep

biding my time

waiting for spring to spring

waiting for something

always waiting

snow on the ground

snow in the trees

TV sounds

my clothes are clean

new place, old feelings

the prison gates have been opened

a new day has dawned

here's hopin'

i stay in my cell, shades drawn

still in chains, holding the keys

released, refusing to leave

the only home

i've ever known

feeling incapable of...

too many things for just one sentence

feeling...

no
no more feelings
feelings are the problem

un-feel, non-feel

is there an on-and-off switch?
or is this hamster wheel forever?

circles have no end, no beginning

beginning to think...

no
no more thinking
thinking is the problem too

un-think, non-think

can i get off this ride?
pretty please, with a side of fries?

i once was blind, but now i see

and part of me wishes i didn't
part of me misses being blind

everything was so simple

yeah, i was miserable
but i had a mission

get high and stay high

hopeless, and yet, a focus
a honed sense of clarity

purpose, even

and now? it's all a mystery

like, yeah, i'm clean and sober
but so what? it's not enough
to be free *from* something

what have i been set free *for*?

like, *why* have i been given this freedom?

why me?

please
somebody
anybody
tell me why

why am *i* still alive?

the only difference i see
between now and then—

i'm not high when
my friends die

not yet

if i get high, if i don't
if i get high, if i don't

like petals from a rose

she loves me, she loves me not
she loves me, she loves me not

either way

i lose

you of little faith, why are you so afraid? [21]

is it me? is it all in my head?

there's gotta be more than this

new place, old feelings
no fight or flight left
i freeze

waiting for something
always waiting
fuck
waiting doesn't make me unstuck
the more i wait, the more stuck i become
double fuck
still numb
frozen
trapped
negative thought and self-talk patterns
back to back and back again
triple fuck
who or what can i trust?
certainly not myself
these feelings
these thoughts
all the self-talk
none of the above
quadruple fuck

lies on sale, two for one

so many lies

where's the truth?

i'd pay full price for some

you of little faith, why are you so afraid?

is that supposed to help?

reminding me of my fear
doesn't make it disappear

do you ever say anything else?

just leave me alone

be still for a second, and know—

I

AM

GOD [22]

that's all you got?

i might as well go back to being god

did you ever stop?

(another) epiphany

you alright? Dev asked

i don't even know anymore, i said

what's goin' on?

you serious?

c'mon, man, you know what i mean, you never talk to me anymore

you're never around, i said

don't put this on me, Cam, this isn't about me
it's about you...

it's always about you

ohh-kay, i said

do you have any idea what this past year has been like for me?
do you even care? he asked

what it's been like for you?!

here we go again

what's that s'posed to mean?

Dev paused

look, i know you just lost your best friend, he said
and i'm really sorry, truly, i am
i don't know what that's like...

it's been a hard year for you in general, man, i get it...

and i don't know what it's like bein' you...

but you're not the only one with problems, ya know?

i never said i was

you sure do act like it sometimes

why'd you even ask how i was doing?
i don't need this shit

you're right, i'm sorry, it's just...

never mind, Dev said

what? i asked

nothing, we can talk about it another time

no, what were you gonna say?

do you know why i always hang out at Sarah's now?

why?

because i can relax there

and here? i asked

well, here i'm always tense and on edge

i looked away, biting my tongue

i'm sorry, Cam, i'm not tryin' to hurt your feelings
i know you're doin' your best, and shit, man, you're doin' great
nine months clean now, that's amazing...

i'm so happy for you and proud of you...

but i'm just tired, man

you're tired?

it's been a hard year for me too, Cam…

but we don't have to talk about this now
i don't even know why i brought it up

no, let's talk about your hard year, i wanna hear all about it

Dev glared at me

do you have any idea what it's been like livin' with you? he asked

enlighten me

it's been exhausting, Cam, and i'm talkin' post-rehab
we don't even need to go into before…

there have been so many hopeless days
especially early on when a relapse would happen
and it's back to square one…

it was impossible to have any sort of perspective…

no plausible good scenario to be played out

i haven't relapsed in nine months, i said

i'm just startin' at the beginning, he said
you're the one who wanted to talk about this, remember?

i bit my tongue so hard i tasted iron

dealin' with one-eighty shifts in emotions out of nowhere
tryin' to make you feel better all the time
livin' in fear of how you would react
it was so confusing, man…

i started questioning things about myself, personalizing it

i thought it was something i was doing wrong
even though my actions had nothing to do with it...

before i knew it, i had all these resentments...

all my time and energy were focused on you
and i didn't see any good comin' from it
no acknowledgment of the hard work and enduring i had done...

but, looking back, the high-intensity moments were easy, relatively
it was the mundane, nothing-seems-to-be-changing moments
when it was hardest to see the light...

eventually, every day seemed gray...

so, yeah, like i said, it's been highly tense and stressful...

not to mention, i had my own stuff i was dealin' with
it's not like my life stopped so i could focus a hundred percent on you
even though that's what it felt like you expected...

don't get me wrong, Cam, i'm grateful to be part of your recovery
i wouldn't trade anything we've been through
but i'm just tired...

i hope you don't take anything i said the wrong way
you know i'm here for you and i'd do anything for you...

i'm just tryin' to be honest

i was crying at this point

i'm sorry, bro, i am, Dev said
i'm not blaming you or tryin' to cause you any more stress
but sometimes it feels like you don't even see me...

like i'm just a character in your life that has no feelings or needs
and every time Mom or Dad calls, we basically just talk about you

so, yeah, i've been spendin' more time with Sarah
because she actually sees me...

it just seems like you have no idea what i've done for you
like you just take me totally for granted
and it hurts my feelings, man...

i don't need a huge thank-you or anything like that
i'm your brother and that's what brothers are for
but it's not all about you, man

i'm sorry, Dev...

i'm a piece o' shit

no, you're not, Cam, and you don't have to apologize
i shouldn't have even laid all this on you right now...

so i'm the one that's sorry

i'm glad you told me...

but yikes, that was a lot

Dev laughed

i still love you, Cameron

i love you too, Dev...

and again, i'm sorry...

and please...

and thank you...

and you're welcome, i said

it's your world, man, i'm just the roommate, Dev said, still laughing *damn straight,* i said, laughing too

side note, i'm all over the place—
first i'm angry, then i'm crying, now i'm laughing

yeah, you're a mess, Dev said
but no, seriously, it's a good thing...

you're real now, bro
you're real...

do you know what i mean? he asked

i smiled

yeah...

actually, i think i do

(still) becoming

i'm thinking every thought
and feeling every feeling

even when it hurts the worst
i'm learning to be me

and what it means

to be real

it takes a long time

that's why it doesn't happen often
to people who break easily
or have sharp edges
or have to be carefully kept

generally, by the time you are real
most of your hair has been loved off
and your eyes drop out
and you get loose in the joints
and very shabby

but these things don't matter at all

because once you are real
you can't be ugly

except to people who don't understand

the keys

i wonder…

it's not your fault, Andy had said

if i knew…

it's not your fault

what would i, could i, should i do?

it's not your fault

this ain't *Good Will Hunting*

there's nothing you could have done

it's…

not…

my…

ffffuuuuuck

unlock the door

step outside

onto the porch

into the sun

i see a rainbow

a portion of one

faintly, but it's there

take off my shades

straining my eyes

scanning the sky

a piercing stare

but it's gone

must've been

the glare

jack-in-the-box

remember—there is hope...

no matter what...

there is always *hope*

would she still say there is?

i bet she would

Rachel had cancer when she was a kid
doctors said she wouldn't live past six

now i'm twenty-five...

every day's a gift, a precious blessing, she'd said

i try to never forget

    all around the cobbler's bench

    the monkey chased the weasel

    the monkey thought 'twas all in good fun

    pop! goes the weasel [23]

no one can change what happened, Andy had said

and it's gonna hurt for a while, a long while...

but you still have a choice, Cameron
you worked hard for that choice...

if you pick up again, you will lose that power to choose...

you're doing it, buddy, one day at a time
stay in today, don't worry about tomorrow
going back out won't make anything better

it never did

one day at a time

things'll get better again

      up and down the King's Road

      in and out the Eagle

      that's the way the money goes

      pop! goes the weasel

Cameron, if you're like me...

your brain needs *washing,* Andy had said

we don't always know what's best
look where our best ideas got us...

there's so much i don't understand, Cameron
i have more questions than answers...

but one thing i know for sure—
i'm staying sober, which is all i need to know

can i get an *amen?!*

i can't do it alone, buddy
and neither can you...

i can't explain it either, but that's the point...

if i could do either of those things
why would i need a Power greater than me?

      a penny for a spool of thread

      a penny for a needle

      that's the way the money goes

      pop! goes the weasel

this is your life, man! Dev had said

and there's a whole lotta livin' left for you to do...

i don't know about you, but i don't wanna waste another second

me neither, Dev

it's a miracle we're still alive

and you can't explain miracles...

you don't need a rainbow, Cam—
your life *is the sign*

      Jimmy's got the whooping cough

      and Timmy's got the measles

      that's the way the story goes

      pop! goes the weasel

*for real, though, i don't wanna keep usin' this disease as an excuse
i don't wanna keep hurtin' every single person in my life...*

i don't wanna lose anyone else, Everett had said

damn, that hits a little different now

i can see it in your eyes, he'd said

you want this, and you have a reason, a why...

*any time you're tempted, have a craving, whatever
just keep comin' back to the why*

i want this

i got this

i *so* got this

i've no time to wait and sigh

no patience to wait 'til by and by

kiss me quick, i'm off, goodbye!

pop! goes the mother fuckin' weasel

where would i be

without the people in my life?

sometimes, people leave
die
or just plain suck

how am i any different?

i've left, i'll prob'ly leave again
i could've died, i will someday
and—well, you catch my drift

thank God for the people, no less
who put up with me and my mess

apparently, i'm worth the risk

let me venture a guess—
you're not that different from me
and there's at least one person who…

you know where i'm goin' with this

people—why even try?

because of where i'd be
without the people in my life

people who thought i was worth the try

who still think i am

who will 'til i die

(aside)

maybe
the word
"worthy"
comes from
"worth the try"

WORTH ~~the tr~~Y

you know where i'm goin' with this, right?

even if you do

it's hard to believe
and easy to forget

but that doesn't mean
it's any less true

let's say it together—

WE

ARE

WORTHY

that being said

why do some people get sober and others don't?

why do some people die and others don't?

i still wanna know

though i suppose
i never will

aren't we all worthy?

i think so, even still

we don't always get to know
why things happen
like Dev said

there's so much i don't understand
i have more questions than answers
like Andy said

nevertheless, i choose to believe
i'm alive and clean
because of YOU

you are my reason

and yet, like Andy also said
it's not entirely selfless

it's about me too

but it's a good kind of selfish

speaking of Andy

maybe we do the same readings
and say the same phrases
and pray the same prayers
at all the meetings
for the simple reason
that important things in life
bear repeating

not once
not twice
but as long as we're breathing

the truth can be hard to believe
and easy to forget

but that doesn't mean
it's any less true

your brain needs *washing*

and lies don't scrub off easily

real change takes time

maybe even a whole life, i surmise

but it starts all at once
whenever you decide

snow on the ground

snow in the trees

TV off

i'm done waiting

it's...

not...

my...

fault

repeat it over and over
it's not my fault, it's not my fault

even when i don't believe it, i repeat it
it's not my fault

there's nothing i could have done

i'm not God, i can't save anyone

sometimes the truth kinda sucks

random thought

i used to own a lime-green notebook
i wrote in it every day

the first rule of being a professional liar—
you gotta keep your lies straight

i no longer own a lime-green notebook

i'm retired

i'm never goin' back

so many people—gone too soon

their lives will *not* have been lost in vain

so long as blood flows red in my veins
whatever the cost
come what may

i will stand

head held high
shoulders, knees, and toes pointed forward
the story's not over
blank pages left to write
can't change the past
but today i have a choice
my choices today can change the future
forget the sutures
leave the wound open
i have a voice
i will bleed these words

a token to those whose breathing has ceased

whose voices—no longer heard

this is *our* voice
we *will* be heard

these words—far from being absurd or devoid of worth
these words, full of pain, have purpose and power
these words have a name
and it's HOPE

and it's ours

just for today

i *will* stay clean
i *will* stay sober

this is my *life*
it's bigger than me, though
i know that's right

i once was lost, but now am found
was blind, but now—*now* i see

i can only keep what i give away
with every breath i take
i will proclaim

this amazing grace that saved

a wretch

like me

so that others might live

so that others might get

free

EPILOGUE

what else can i say?

Dev and Sarah got engaged!

my younger older brother
in so many ways

no champagne, but i'll raise a glass
a toast to my favorite couple

my addict-ass already practicing—
just water for me, please

remembering the way Rachel said it
when the waitress asked

i never did hear back

but i'm done waiting
no more expectations

no hard feelings either
i wish her the best

i'm blessed to have known her
she really did help me get sober

i'm forever indebted

to Everett too

still think about him every day

damn near drove myself insane
self-proclaimed detective

never cracked the case

whatever happened in the end
today i know it's not my fault

he's finally at rest

he *will* live on

Andy and i still goin' strong
still meet once a week

my sponsor turned friend

God knows i need more of them
i said that at the beginning

now that this ride is ending
i see i've always had plenty

sometimes one is enough

i'm grateful for everyone
who's come alongside

the ones who stayed
and the ones who left

the ones who lived
and the ones who died

my family

my friends

my life—

the ride is just beginning

people are just people
but the "just" can be deceiving

either way, i'm not afraid
not even a little bit

okay, maybe still a little

but i don't have to give in
to the fear within
i won't

even if i never see
a rainbow again
i know

there is *always* hope

'cause i'm still here

and you are with me

you'll always be

my reason why

my hope, unseen

i mean, i got like *twelve months* sober now

somehow, someway
by the grace of God

and life is good

even when it's not

i never thought
i'd live to see the day

ONE YEAR sober, dawg!

skip, hop, hooray

even now, i only have today

but every day i stay clean
is a pretty good day

a miracle, even

even if i can't explain it

that's what makes it
a miracle, remember?

i try to never forget

any of it

what an amazing gift

what being clean feels like today

ENDNOTES

1. Selections/excerpts (sometimes appearing with minor modifications) of lyrics from the hymn "Amazing Grace" (authored by John Newton, 1779) are used throughout this work, but hereafter a note is not included. Selections/excerpts are based on lyrics found at https:// hymnary.org/text/amazing_grace_how_sweet_the_sound.

2. Based on Exodus 3:14.

3. Selections/excerpts (sometimes appearing with minor modifications) of lyrics from the hymn "Silent Night, Holy Night" (authored by Joseph Mohr; stanzas two and four translated by anonymous, and stanzas one and three translated by J. Freeman young) are used here and elsewhere in this work, but hereafter a note is not included. Selections/excerpts are based on lyrics found at https://hymnary.org/text/ silent_night_holy_night_all_is_calm_all.

4. Lyrics from the "ABC Song," which was first published and copyrighted in 1835 by Charles Bradlee. Based on lyrics found at https:// allnurseryrhymes.com/the-alphabet-song.

5. Based on Luke 4: 5–7, King James Version (KJV), Holy Bible.

6. Psalm 23 is quoted herein in its entirety.

7. What follows are paraphrases of Steps 1 through 3, based on the 12 Steps of Alcoholics Anonymous (A.A.), which can be found at http:// gsowatch.aamo.info/1939/uslaw.htm#manu. Alcoholics Anonymous and A.A. are registered trademarks of A.A. World Services, Inc. Paraphrases of Steps 4 through 12 are included elsewhere in this work, but a note is not included.

8. Inspired by *The Velveteen Rabbit*, a British children's book written by Margery Williams, illustrated by William Nicholson, and first published by the George H. Doran Company in 1922. I include a direct quote from *The Velveteen Rabbit* elsewhere in this work, but a note is not included.

9. "Your book" is a reference to the book *Alcoholics Anonymous,* fourth edition, Alcoholics Anonymous World Services, Inc., New York

City, 2001; this book is commonly referred to as the Big Book and is referenced elsewhere in this work, but a note is not included.

10. "All work and no play makes…" is an allusion to the proverb; the rest of the sentence is "Jack a dull boy" (not included in this work). The modern saying first appeared in James Howell's *Proverbs* (1659), but you may know it from *The Shining*, a 1980 horror film produced and directed by Stanley Kubrick, who also wrote the film (along with Diane Johnson) based on the Stephen King novel (1977) with the same title.

11. Based on Psalm 46:2.

12. Based on Romans 8:28.

13. Excerpt from Romans 8:24.

14. "Plaster rolls up like a scroll" is based on Revelation 6:14, and "roof splits open, Red Sea-style" is inspired by Exodus 14:16, 21-22.

15. "Before you were even born, I was" is based on John 8:58. "The first, the last" is based on Isaiah 44:6 and 48:12, as well as Revelation 1:17, 2:8, and 22:13. "You will know the truth, and the truth will set you free" is an excerpt from John 8:32. "The people walking in darkness have seen a great light" is an excerpt from Isaiah 9:2. "The light shines in the darkness, and the darkness has not overcome it" is John 1:5.

16. Based on Revelation 13:18.

17. Based on Matthew 8:12, 13:42, 13:50, 22:13, 24:51, and 25:30, as well as Luke 13:28.

18. This is in no way meant to be derogatory toward lesbians or anyone else in the LGBTQ+ community.

19. Based on Genesis 3:4.

20. The question that appears on the screen is the infamous Netflix question.

21. Excerpt from Matthew 8:26. Also appears elsewhere in this work but a note is not included.

22. Based on Psalm 46:10.

23. "Pop! Goes the Weasel" is a nursery rhyme and singing game that originated in England, possibly as early as the 18th century.

I quote a contemporary U.S. version in its entirety herein (sometimes with minor modifications), based on lyrics found at https://en.wikipedia.org/wiki/Pop_Goes_the_Weasel.

ACKNOWLEDGMENTS

First off, thank you to YOU for reading this. I hope you enjoyed the ride.

Thank you to my family and friends who read early drafts, provided feedback, and helped make *Clean* what it is today. Thank you to everyone who encouraged me along the way. You know who you are, and I couldn't have done it without you.

Thank you also to Luminare Press for helping make *Clean* what it is today, and moreover for helping me turn my dream of publishing a book into a reality. You guys are awesome.

Thank you to everyone who supported (and continues to support) me in my own recovery journey. I can't do this alone, and I'm immensely grateful for my people—you know who you are, and I got mad love for each and every one of you.

Thanks be to God, without whom I wouldn't be where I am today, without whom I wouldn't even *be* at all. God is g double-o d good, all the time.

AUTHOR'S NOTE

I don't know if alcoholism or drug addiction has affected your life in some way, shape, or form, but I do know that you have a story. Everyone has a story, and our stories are powerful when we own them and share them.

Let's be honest, though—we're all addicted to something; some addictions are simply less visible, less destructive, or more socially acceptable than others. But I digress.

I hope that by sharing some of my story I encourage others to do the same. Yes, *Clean* is a fictionalized version of my story, but it is still my story insofar as it attempts to convey (through the narrator, Cameron) what was happening on the inside during parts of my own journey through active addiction and early recovery, even though the external details of my journey vary from those of Cameron's.

However, while *Clean* is inspired by true events and is arguably (in a sense) a true story about addiction and recovery, it is ultimately a work of fiction.

I'll let you decide if that matters or not. But I digress (again).

For my fellow addicts and alcoholics, specifically those of you who are actively using and/or drinking, I hope my story helps you see (and believe) that another way of life is possible. "With God, all things are possible" (Matthew 19:26).

Some of you likely don't believe in God or gave up on Him long ago, but He hasn't given up on you. He sees you, knows you, and loves you still—and He always will. Whether you believe that or not, please don't give up on yourself.

We (addicts and alcoholics especially, but human beings in general) are experts when it comes to justification, rationalization, manipulation, and deception (particularly self-deception). Sometimes the most courageous thing we can do is admit we have a problem and need help. It's a sign of strength, not weakness, and it's never too late.

Now's the time to get honest with yourself and others. It's gonna be uncomfortable and scary and will likely go against every natural instinct you have, but it may also save your life. So what are you waiting for?

You are so much more than an "addict" or "alcoholic." These are not identity statements or labels. I understand the chronic nature of these diseases and the rationale behind continuing to refer to yourself as such (even once you're in recovery), but you are so much more than your afflictions, predispositions, and struggles.

Your true self is waiting to be discovered, and everything you need to get started is right here, right now. So I'll ask again, what are you waiting for?

Abundant resources are available to help (recovery groups, treatment centers, counseling, etc.), and you don't have to do it alone. In fact, you can't do it alone.

It doesn't matter what happened in the past; all that matters is what you do now.

To my fellow addicts and alcoholics in early recovery—I applaud your courage and just wanna encourage you to keep going. I promise you, it does get easier. It has for me at least.

To the "old timers" (as they say in the rooms)—I wanna thank you for giving us younger folks in recovery a vision of what's possible.

For those of you who know someone struggling with drug and/or alcohol addiction (I'm talking primarily to family members, but this can apply more broadly), a variety of resources are available to help you as well. And if you take away nothing else from this book, please know this—it's NOT your fault.

Whoever you are, whatever you've been through, and whatever you're going through, I hope you know you're not alone. You are never alone. And there is always hope.

There's a lot more I could say, but lemme wrap this up by thanking you again for reading *Clean*. For real, it means more to me than you know.

Writing and publishing a book has been a dream of mine for years, but some part of me never thought I'd see that dream come to fruition.

Then again, I never thought I'd get sober, but by the grace of God here I am—earlier this year I celebrated my five-year sober-versary!

So dream big, my friends, and do not be afraid. This is your life!

Your life matters. YOU matter.

And there is always hope.

Much love,
Michael

For more information, visit
www.michaelrebellino.com

Made in United States
Orlando, FL
03 January 2022

12861728R00174